Stephen Crane:

SULLIVAN COUNTY TALES
AND SKETCHES

Stephen Crane:

SULLIVAN COUNTY TALES
AND SKETCHES

Edited and with an Introduction by
R. W. Stallman

THE IOWA STATE UNIVERSITY PRESS
Ames, Iowa

© 1968 R. W. Stallman

Composed and printed by
The Iowa State University Press
Ames, Iowa, U.S.A.

First edition, 1968

Second printing, 1969

Standard Book Number: 8138-1625-4

Library of Congress Catalog Card Number: 68-17485

FOR BILL

ACKNOWLEDGEMENTS

TO the "three gentlemen who as boys knew the young Stephen Crane at Hartwood, New York, and at Twin Lakes, Pennsylvania"—so reads the dedication of *The New York City Sketches of Stephen Crane,* which I co-edited with E. R. Hagemann (New York, 1966). One of these gentlemen is Mr. L. B. Watson, now age ninety-two, who as a boy knew Stephen Crane during his camping-out visits at Twin Lakes. Mr. Watson came down from Twin Lakes in August of 1962 to dine at the home of Mr. David Balch in Hartwood with Mr. George Dimock, now deceased, and his brother E. J. Dimock, who is still active as a Federal Judge of the United States District Court of New York. The Dimocks knew Crane when they were boys living at Hartwood. They exchanged memories about Crane at Mr. Balch's dinner, while I took notes later utilized in my *Stephen Crane: A Biography* (George Braziller, Inc., 1968).

Judge Dimock in 1966 kindly sent me a press clipping of "The Last of the Mohicans" from the Dimock family papers preserved since the early 1890's. On the same page of this undated and unidentified press clipping was an advertisement that the Fall River Line's popular steamers *Plymouth* and *Providence* would resume Sunday excursions to Manhattan commencing April 3. As Sunday for April 3 belonged to the year 1892, this unsigned Crane sketch must have appeared in some New York City newspaper—either the *Tribune* or the *Herald*—prior to that date and subsequent to the press clipping's dateline: "Hartwood, Sullivan County, N.Y., Feb. 15."

The New York Public Library's Research Librarian, Mr. Harold Merklen, promptly located "The Last of the Mohicans" in the New York *Tribune* for Sunday, February

21, 1892. Next, I hired my former graduate student Miss Kelly Flynn to trace in the *Tribune* sketches bearing that telltale dateline of Hartwood, with the result that five additional unsigned Crane Sullivan County sketches were discovered. Subsequently, copies of the *Tribune* for 1891 and 1893 were searched by Miss Bobby Mason, another University of Connecticut graduate student, but this time without success.

I am thus immeasurably indebted to Judge E. J. Dimock, whose gift of that press clipping initiated what has become the present new edition of *Stephen Crane: Sullivan County Tales and Sketches.*

Here, then, are six new Sullivan County sketches, additions to the Crane canon, of which five are reproduced for the first time. "The Last of the Mohicans" was first reproduced in *American Literature,* 39 (November 1967), 392–96: "Stephen Crane and Cooper's Uncas," by R. W. Stallman.

Another new Sullivan County tale is "Across the Covered Pit," where the cave is called Mammoth Cave (misspelled in Edith Crane's typescript "Manmoth"), not to be confused with the famous Mammoth Cave in Kentucky. It is the same cave described in "Four Men in a Cave," an early draft of which locates the game of poker in the woods, not in the cave.

Another Sullivan County sketch—not reproduced here—is "Jack," a dog sketch extant in three unfinished drafts, of which one version was reproduced from the holograph manuscript as the cover to *Fine Arts Magazine* (University of Connecticut), Vol. 6, 1961. The dog "Jack" was the black mastiff which Edmund Crane's children used to take along with them to a summer camp on the Mongaup River in Sullivan County.

The title "Sullivan County Sketches" was first designated by Cora Taylor ("Mrs. Stephen Crane") in Stephen's *Last Words* (London, 1902) for two tales: "The Mesmeric Mountain" and "Four Men in a Cave." As this last tale had appeared in the New York *Tribune* in 1892 for July 3, it formed Crane's "first words," not his "last words."

Melvin Schoberlin erred in not including "The Snake" in his *Sullivan County Sketches of Stephen Crane* (1949), since it was included as a Sullivan County sketch in Wilson

Follett's *The Work of Stephen Crane,* Vol. XI (1926) and in Vincent Starrett's edition of *Maggie: A Girl of the Streets and Other Stories* (1933). Follett's *Work* collected four Sullivan County pieces, and Schoberlin's book ten; here are nineteen.

For grant in aid of research on this volume I am indebted to the University of Connecticut Research Foundation. I am grateful also to Mrs. Sol Wollman for typing the manuscript, and to Mr. William Schrugg, who, while in my graduate seminar (Spring 1966), studied the Sullivan County tales and sketches in relation to the whole body of Crane's works.

I wish to thank Miss Roberta Smith, reference librarian at the University of Connecticut, for her constant and invaluable aid on my Crane researches during the past seventeen years.

I also wish to thank Miss Elizabeth Ryall of the Manuscript Division of the University of Virginia Library for providing copies of the holograph manuscripts for "The Snake" and "The Holler Tree" from the Clifton Waller Barrett Crane Collection.

This book is illustrated by the pen-and-ink drawings of "W. W.," an artist who prefers to remain anonymous.

R. W. STALLMAN

CONTENTS

Acknowledgements   vii

Introduction   3

THE TALES AND SKETCHES

The Last of the Mohicans
    New York *Tribune:* February 21, 1892   27

Hunting Wild Hogs
    New York *Tribune:* February 28, 1892   31

The Last Panther
    New York *Tribune:* April 3, 1892   43

Sullivan County Bears
    New York *Tribune:* April 19, 1892   49

The Way in Sullivan County
    New York *Tribune:* May 8, 1892   59

Bear and Panther
    New York *Tribune:* July 17, 1892   63

Killing His Bear
    New York *Tribune:* July 31, 1892   67

Four Men in a Cave
    New York *Tribune:* July 3, 1892   71

Across the Covered Pit
    Bulletin New York Public Library: January 1957 79

The Octopush
    New York *Tribune:* July 10, 1892   85

A Ghoul's Accountant
New York *Tribune:* July 17, 1892   91

The Black Dog
New York *Tribune:* July 24, 1892   97

A Tent in Agony
Cosmopolitan: December 1892   105

An Explosion of Seven Babies
Holograph MS in the Barrett Crane Collection   109

The Cry of a Huckleberry Pudding
Syracuse *University Herald:* December 23, 1892   115

The Holler Tree
Holograph MS in the Barrett Crane Collection   123

The Snake
Holograph MS in the Barrett Crane Collection   133

THE FABLES

The Mesmeric Mountain
Last Words: 1902   141

How the Donkey Lifted the Hills
Pocket Magazine: June 1897   147

Introduction

INTRODUCTION

DURING summers and school vacations young
Stephen Crane rode his circus pony Pudgy on
the Asbury Park beach or frequented the forested
mountains of Hartwood, New York, tramping the
woods or fishing for pickerel in Pond Eddy.

Brother William Howe Crane, who had settled
as a lawyer in 1882 in Port Jervis, New York, was
president of the Hartwood Club in Sullivan County.
The Hartwood Club was syndicated by wealthy own-
ers for hunting and fishing on 6,000 acres of moun-
tainous timber and lakes (with hunting rights on all
but 1,000 acres), and from the Dimock Syndicate
Judge Crane obtained 3,500 acres for his legal serv-
ices to the Hartwood Club. They enjoyed a com-
modius clubhouse up in the hills from the pond in
Hartwood Park which is today known as "The
Stephen Crane Pond."

Judge Crane, who wore whiskers like a horned
owl and was always known as the Judge, took
Stephen with him on some of his Hartwood Club
hunting parties. Once when he was standing on a
"runway" for deer he suddenly encountered a herd
of wild hogs. "Turning quickly, he caught a glimpse
of a brown body and fired. They carried home a
wild hog weighing 200 pounds. The carcass was inspected, photographed and sketched. A magnificent
skin, with stuffed head, now hangs in the clubhouse

at Hartwood Park," says his twenty-year-old brother Stevie in "Hunting Wild Hogs." The hero of the final hog hunt was Lew Boyd, a famous bear hunter, and with him was "a young man with a bulldog . . . who said his dog would fight anything." That is undoubtedly Stevie Crane, whom we detect again in "The Way in Sullivan County" as the city man listening awesomely to the natives telling their tall tales.

One can buy sawlogs from a native and take his word that the bargain is square, but ask the same man how many deer he has killed in his lifetime and he will stop working, take a seat on the snake-fence and paralyze the questioner with a figure that would look better than most of the totals to the subscription lists for monuments to national heroes. The inhabitants grow up to regard each other with painful suspicion. So there is very little field for the expert liars among their fellows. They must keep to a certain percentage or they will lose caste, but there is little pleasure in it for them because everybody knows everybody else. The only real enjoyment is when the unoffending city man appears. They welcome him with joyful cries. After he recovers from a paroxysm of awe and astonishment he seizes his pen and, with flashing eye and trembling, eager fingers, writes those brief but lurid sketches which fascinate and charm the reading public while the virtuous bushwhacker, whittling a stick near by, smiles in his own calm and sweet fashion.

As a spinner of hunting yarns Crane himself was something of a skilled Sullivan County "liar." In his sketch "The Last Panther" he tells the story of a man named Calvin Bush, "the prince of panther-killers," according to an old authority. Bush aimed a blow of his hatchet at a panther's head.

The animal dodged and caught the handle in its teeth. It wrenched the implement from the hunter's hand with the

utmost ease, and then dropped it to fight the dog, which
had begun a noisy attack in the rear. While the panther
was mutilating the dog, Bush loaded his gun and shot it
through the head. He always carried a crooked finger,
which was made by the panther's teeth when it grasped
the hatchet-handle.

From "the old and weather-beaten inhabitants
of the pines and boulders of Sullivan County" Crane
picked up at the firesides of old homesteads the historical legends of that region and of the neighboring
counties. Their yarns he verified in certain books
written by learned men who had "dived into piles of
mouldy documents and dusty chronicles to establish
their facts." One of these chronicles was J. E. Quinlan's *History of Sullivan County* (1873), which
Crane obviously knew because he derived from
Quinlan's story of the murder of rich Hasbrouck the
name of his soldier Hasbrouck in *The Red Badge of
Courage:* "That young Hasbrouck, he makes a good
off'cer. He ain't afraid 'a nothin'."

Quinlan relates the hunting exploits of early
settlers at the turn of the nineteenth century and
even prior to the War of the Revolution. While
Joseph and Patty Griffin collected toll at their Neversink River bridge of Oakland, another pioneer of
the Oakland settlement named Isaac Moore passed
that way and saw a strange animal by the roadside.
"His dog soon treed the beast, and Moore shot it.
It was a panther." Moore loved to kill panthers, and
he loved quite as well to tell a good story.

Like all dwellers in those woods where the game
was abundant, Zephaniah Drake was fond of forest
sports and so excelled all others in shooting wild
beasts "that he imagined himself the champion rifle-
man of his neighborhood." He founded, in 1793,

Draketown, a part of Forestburg. Nearby are Beaver Pond and Panther Pond. Forestburg is situated on the high ridges between the Neversink and the Mongaup and is drained by the affluents of those rivers. Nearby is Mohican Lake, no doubt named after Mohican Indian settlers thereabouts. Forestburg becomes "Fowlerville" in one of Crane's sketches. To the southeast is Hartwood, named in honor of the Reverend Mr. Hart.

At Oakland, in the lower valley of the Neversink, Simeon Barber won the sobriquet of Bear Killer by his adventures in hunting. However, he was coaxed into marriage by the flabby charms of a faded siren, and then she absconded with his hoarded money ($300), just as she had plotted to do before enticing the old hunter into forgetting his guns and bear traps. The great Bear Killer thus himself fell into a trap, says Quinlan.

At Panther Pond wolves had their nocturnal trysting place, but on scenting food at Joseph Norris' log house a mile away they boldly approached and in packs slaughtered his cattle. Norris and his children spent "a night of terror" surrounded by these yelling and snarling wolves. In the daytime Norris was challenged by a stray bear or by a defiant rattlesnake, always ready for battle. Not so formidable was the bear—he shuffled off at his utmost speed. Crane describes the bear as timid; when pursued by a hound the bear (in "Killing His Bear") ran "like a frightened kitten."

Not far from Oakland is a narrow canyon with high and perpendicular rock walls siding it, and through it flows the outlet of a mountain pond which at one point becomes a subterranean waterfall. There in 1863 James Brooks found two wild-

cats in their den, boldly entered their lair and killed
them. Crane (in "The Last Panther") tells the story
of a Negro boy who crawled into a cave to confront
the yellow-green eyes of a huge panther sequestered
in its den in a ledge of rocks.

What gives weight to the fireside yarns that
seem like tall tales is that they can be verified by
dusty chronicles such as Quinlan's *History of Sullivan County*. Crane puts it metaphorically in "The
Last of the Mohicans."[1] He says: "This gives the
great Sullivan County thunderbolt immense weight.
And they hurl it at no less a head than that which
once evolved from its inner recesses the famous
Leatherstocking Tales." When you tell them about
the noble savage of Cooper's fiction, they shake
"metaphorical fists" at Cooper's *The Last of the Mohicans* and scornfully sneer. The old story-tellers of
Sullivan County insist that the original for Cooper's
fictionalized bronze god Uncas ended his life there,
not as a noble warrior who had yearned after the
blood of his enemies but as a derelict begging from
house to house a drink of the white man's rum.
There was nothing noble about him. "He was a veritable 'poor Indian.' He dragged through his
wretched life in helpless misery."

Crane's otherwise mysterious nickname "Indians" for his artist friends in New York City harks

---

[1] Unsigned, "The Last of the Mohicans" bears Crane's unmistaka-
ble signature in his device of contrast and in his metaphoric style. As
the story-telling historians of Sullivan County shake "metaphorical
fists," so too does Henry Fleming in *The Red Badge of Courage*. At
the death of Jim Conklin, "The youth turned, with sudden, livid rage,
toward the battle-field. He shook his fist. He seemed about to deliver
a philippic. 'Hell. . . .' "

The death scene of Jim Conklin has its echo in the Sullivan
County fable called "The Mesmeric Mountain": "The summit was a
blaze of red wrath." In "The Holler Tree" the pudgy man "cursed
in an unhappy vein as he was confronted by the little man's grins.
The latter seemed about to deliver an oration. . . ."

back to his familiarity with the legendary and fallen Uncas of Sullivan County. At Claverack College (1888–1890) he nicknamed Earl T. Reeve from Rushville, Indiana, the "Rushville Indian." He also called him "Sioux," although Reeve was the richest boy in school. Crane's artist friends at the old Needham Building on East 23rd Street, which housed the Art Students' League until October 1892, were "Indians" because—like Uncas—they wore ragged garments and begged or borrowed their food, drink, and bed. So, too, did Crane himself. He declared in 1893 that he would sell his future for $23. He, too, was a veritable "poor Indian." London journalists who exploited Crane's hospitality during his English years by uninvited intrusions at Ravensbrook Villa in Surrey were cursed by his sobriquet "Indians," and when seven men overstayed their visit Crane fled to a London hotel for two days to finish some work and wrote Acton Davies (December 5, 1897) that "some of these Comanche braves seem to think I am running a free lunch-counter."

Brother William Howe Crane wrote Stephen at Brede Manor in Sussex (November 7, 1899) that a copy of Addison's *Spectator* should be sent to his daughter Helen, then at school in Lausanne (Switzerland), so as to edify her in moral conduct. "I do not know of any reading that inculcates a love of truth more effectively [than Addison's eighteenth-century essays in the *Spectator*], unless it may be *The Deerslayer*." Although Crane's "List of Books/ Brede Place" contained no book by James Fenimore Cooper, he obviously knew his Cooper. In "War Memories" (1899) he wrote that the Cuban pickets were "in fact, of the stuff of Fenimore Cooper's Indians, only they made no preposterous orations."

He described the skirmish at Cuzca in Cuba like "quail shooting." Stephen's niece Edith said her uncle "was a good shot. He seemed to enjoy target practice and tramped through the woods a great deal at Hartwood, but he was not as keen about hunting and fishing as my father [Edmund Crane]."

Although he was to spend most of his life imagining or experiencing battlefields, he had a deep respect for life and was opposed to hunting animals down wantonly. He admired the courage not of the hunter but of the hunted, and in some of his Sullivan County tales and sketches he shows up the cowardice of the hunter. Hunting is warfare, too. "Youths grew up with desire for fame, and they took rifles and went to seek it in the woods. A hardy race of huntsmen made terrible war on the game," says Crane in "Sullivan County Bears." He spoofs at the hunters who, hiding in a cave, wait it out until a panther claws to death a bear: "the brilliant-minded and philosophical hunters dangled their heels and smilingly looked on until the panther finished the bear. Then they shot the victor." With that wry commentary Crane ends his sketch, "The Way in Sullivan County: A Study in the Evolution of the Hunting Yarn." Here he exposes the gap between the hunter of fiction, the Sullivan County bushwackers who thought themselves "very great men indeed," and the hunter of reality. Crane's sympathies are with the bear.

WHILE ATTENDING Claverack College (1888–1890), Lafayette College (Autumn 1890), and Syracuse University (Spring 1891), Stephen spent his sum-

mers at his mother's house in Asbury Park, New
Jersey, where Mrs. Crane finally settled after the
death of the Reverend Dr. Jonathan Townley Crane
(he died in Port Jervis on February 16, 1880, when
Stephen was seven). Her son Jonathan Townley, Jr.,
began a news agency there in 1882 and furnished the
New York *Tribune* and other papers their "shore
news," with brother Wilbur and youngster Stephen
aiding him. Mrs. Crane wrote unsigned *Tribune* reports about Methodist revivalist meetings at nearby
Ocean Grove until she fell seriously ill for several
months in 1886. As early as 1888 Stephen wrote
such unsigned *Tribune* shore news as "Gay Bathing
Suit and Novel Both Must Go."

"I began writing for newspapers when I was
16 [at Asbury Park in 1888]," Crane wrote the Editor of *The Critic*. "At 18 I did my first fiction for
the N.Y. Sunday *Tribune*—sketches. At 20 I began
Maggie & finished it when I was somewhat beyond
21. Later in the same year [1893] I began *The R. B.
of Courage* and finished it some months after my
22nd birthday. The *Black Riders* poems were written in that year." However, some of the *Black
Riders* poems were written in late 1891, and his first
fiction for the *Tribune*—the Sullivan County pieces
—was done in 1892 when he was 20, not 18.

In the summer of 1891 Stephen's brother Townley, known as the "Shore Fiend," told Willis Fletcher
Johnson that his younger brother had some writings
he'd like to have him see, and as Johnson—day editor of the *Tribune*—had been a friend of the Crane
family ever since his own student days at Pennington
Seminary when the Reverend Dr. J. T. Crane was
its principal or president, he invited Stephen to dis-

cuss his writings with him at the West End Hotel, the rendezvous of Asbury Park newspaper correspondents where Johnson was staying. Shy and reticent, Stephen called on him and exposed two sketches, each of about two thousand words, which struck Johnson as "fantastic and impressionistic fiction sketches." They were his first Sullivan County sketches. "I was very favorably impressed by them and told him so, and at once accepted them for use in the Sunday supplement of *The Tribune.*" Johnson says that the series began to appear in the *Tribune* in 1891, but nothing datelined Hartwood appeared there until February 21, 1892, with the first of the Sullivan County sketches, "The Last of the Mohicans." Not until then did young Stephen earn the *Tribune's* space rate of six dollars per column.

Johnson says that Crane brought him "a big bundle of manuscript and asked me to read it. I found it to be not a Sullivan County sketch, but a tale of the slums of New York; the first draft of *Maggie: A Girl of the Streets.*" However, Johnson's "big bundle of manuscript" indicates that Crane brought him not the first draft but the nearly completed novel in the summer of 1892, not in 1891 as Johnson remembers it.[2] Crane boasted to Wallis McHarg: "I wrote it in two days before Christmas" —in 1891. However, Clarence Loomis Peaslee declared in 1896 that Crane discussed *Maggie* with some of his acquaintances while at Syracuse University, and another Delta Upsilon fraternity brother, Frank W. Noxon, reaffirmed the fact that *Maggie,*

---

[2] "The Launching of Stephen Crane," *Literary Digest International Book Review*, 4 (April 1926), pp. 288–90.

"at least in its early form, was wholly or in part written at Syracuse."[3]

At the same time that Crane was writing *Maggie* in 1891 and rewriting it in 1892, he was also writing his Sullivan County pieces. This conjuncture of events has importance in that it contradicts the commonly held assumption that the Sullivan County writings anticipated *Maggie* and *The Red Badge*, whereas the gap between them spans less than a year and in the writing of *Maggie* there was no time gap at all. In largeness of conception and design the gap between these masterworks and his rather inept Sullivan County tales is immense, but the fact remains that he was simultaneously bringing *Maggie* to completion while publishing his Sullivan County pieces in 1892.

THE FIRST important year for Crane's literary career was 1891 when he was 19, because he then began *Maggie* and his first Sullivan County pieces, interviewed Hamlin Garland for the *Tribune* in August ("Howells Discussed at Avon-by-the-Sea"), and fell in love with Miss Helen Trent at Avon. Out of

[3] Noxon in a letter of 1926 which was published in the Chicago *Step Ladder*, 14 (January 1928), pp. 4–9: "The Real Stephen Crane." Reprinted in *Stephen Crane: Letters*, edited by R. W. Stallman and Lillian Gilkes (New York and London, 1960).

Peaslee wrote "Stephen Crane's College Days," *Monthly Illustrator*, 13 (August 1896), pp. 27–31.

Critics who discredit Noxon's testimony on the grounds that it was written 35 years after the event ignore the collaborating evidence of Peaslee's 1896 sketch. John Berryman in his *Stephen Crane* (New York, 1950) suppresses the evidence of Peaslee and Noxon. While admitting that *Maggie* might have been written "even at Syracuse" (page 32), he contradicts this admission by flatly declaring (page 304) that Crane chose "the subject of *Maggie*, his first work, following immediately upon his mother's death"—on December 7, 1891. Berryman prefers it that way because it best fits his Freudian thesis, but the evidence of Peaslee and Noxon cannot be so conveniently dismissed.

that puppy-love romance which Miss Trent cut short by declaring that she was already betrothed, Crane wrote his first poems (in September 1891). The jilted lover retreated to brother Edmund Brian's house at Lake View, New Jersey.

Edmund and Stephen and their mother, then living at Asbury Park, went to Hartwood to attend a party celebrating the newly formed Hartwood Park Association, and on Wednesday, September 30, they signed the club's register. So did William of Port Jervis. This was undoubtedly the last time they were together. The Hartwood Club's register for Friday, October 2 (1891) reads: "Mother Crane caught seven fine pickerel to her own satisfaction and the astonishment of her brood. The next day she caught three more fish in less than an hour."[4]

The year 1892 was important for several reasons: Crane was publishing his Sullivan County series in the Sunday edition of the *Tribune* and re-writing Maggie; he published also in the *Tribune* his first New York City sketch ("The Broken-Down Van," on July 10, 1892); and he made his first appearance in a professional magazine that December with "A Tent in Agony" in *Cosmopolitan Magazine*. That summer he began an ill-fated romance with the unhappily married Lily Brandon Munroe

---

[4] From an unpublished manuscript read as an address to the Minisink Valley Historical Society by Mr. E. J. Dimock in February 1963: "Stephen Crane and the Minisink Valley." Stephen and William signed the Hartwood Club register also in March 1892 and on May 17, 1892.

At the Hartwood Club's party in September-October 1891, Judge Crane's seven-year-old daughter (he had five daughters) was entertained by a member's wife, a lady "whose conventionality was exceptional even in those days. 'You are so fortunate,' said the lady, 'in being able to live all the year round in this lovely country when *we* can only stay for a short vacation.' 'Yes,' replied the wide-eyed child, 'but you know in midsummer Port Jervis is hotter than hell.' "

and played once more the role of puppy-lover. Something of that love affair he recreated in *The Third Violet* (1896), transposing its location, however, from Asbury Park to Hartwood. In "The Pace of Youth" (1895) he described the Asbury Park life which he had absorbed since 1882.

As the Asbury Park season closed on Labor Day, Townley shut down his agency for lack of news then, and Stephen went off to Sullivan County for vacation before returning to school. There and in adjoining Pike County, Pennsylvania, he and some Port Jervis friends tramped the hills and camped out during several summers into 1896. At Twin Lakes in Pike County in August 1894, Crane and Louis Senger wrote and had printed a mock newspaper called *The Pike County Puzzle*. They loaded it with camp yarns and wisecracks for the amusement of their fellow campers, including the "nice girls" from Port Jervis whose parents supervised their tent while themselves residing in a nearby house on Twin Lakes. During that summer Crane was frightened or bitten by a snake, an incident which he recreated in "The Snake" (1896).

In the Sullivan County tales, already published in 1892 in the *Tribune* and in the Syracuse *University Herald,* Louis C. Senger, Jr., figured as "the tall man"; Frederic M. Lawrence, also of Port Jervis, was "the pudgy man." The "little man" was Louis E. Carr, Jr., and the "quiet man" was of course Stephen himself. He seldom spoke, but when he did his talk was as colorful as his poetry and prose.[5] However, as Crane was given to cursing and as the "little

[5] Melvin Schoberlin identifies them in his Introduction to his edition of *The Sullivan County Sketches of Stephen Crane* (Syracuse, New York, 1949). He evidently interviewed Corwin Knapp Linson, cousin of Louis Senger.

man" in several of the tales makes orations or swears "crimson oaths," he identifies with the "little man" quite as much as with the "quiet man."

"I live in Hartwood, Sullivan Co., N.Y., on an estate of 3500 acres belonging to my brother and am distinguished for corduroy trousers and briar-wood pipes. My idea of happiness is the saddle of a good riding horse," Crane wrote his friend John Northern Hilliard from Hartwood on January 2, 1896. Crane was an expert horseman, a good swimmer, and a good shot (he liked to hunt partridge), and he almost became a professional baseball player. "The blessed quiet hills of Hartwood" served him as sanctuary from the life of the city with its formidable challenge to the struggling journalist on Park Row. He was given to signing his address "The Hartwood Club," by which device his letters gained the luster of prosperity, whereas in fact he lived at Edmund's house on the millpond from which Ed cut ice to ship to Port Jervis.

Edmund, during the depression of 1893, probably lost his job with the railroad, for that spring he moved from Lake View to the house on the millpond to become caretaker of the Hartwood Club and general handyman. In a letter to his close friend Willis B. Hawkins, Stephen said that Edmund served as "postmaster, justice-of-the-peace, ice-man, farmer, millwright, blue stone man, lumberman, station agent on the P. J. M. and N. Y. R. R., and many other things which I now forget." The one-track railway serving Port Jervis and Monticello was the Port Jervis, Midland and New York Railroad, of which all that remains at Hartwood today is the old sign: "Beware of the Cars." John Berryman in his *Stephen Crane* (1950) claimed that Hartwood con-

sisted of "a store, a blacksmith shop, and a tavern."
However, according to the Dimock family who lived
there in Crane's day, there never was any store, nor
any blacksmith shop, nor any tavern in Hartwood.

Edmund, fourteen years older than Stephen,
had married Mary L. Fleming in 1883, and her sur-
name is the source of the hero's name in *The Red
Badge of Courage:* Henry Fleming. Mary and Edmund had three daughters (Agnes, Edith, and
Alice), of whom Edith remembers that Uncle Stephen owned a pair of huge skiis and that her sisters

used to delight in watching him, especially when he would
come down the hills dragging the [snow] pile, which would
send a shower of snow over him so we could hardly see him.
He was a delightful playfellow. Sometimes all three of us
would get on the skiis and by lifting our feet at the same
time we could ride along. . . . He played with my sisters
and myself with snowballs too. We attacked him, and he
captured us and marched us around the house with our
arms up. I can remember on this occasion I got tired of
that and cried, much to my Uncle's disgust, and as my
mother laughed I felt disgraced indeed. He never could
play too rough for my sister Agnes, however. She was
always game.[6]

A FEW YEARS after he last saw Mrs. Lily Brandon
Munroe in late August 1892, Crane wrote her:

You know, when I left you [shortly after completing most
of his Sullivan County pieces], I renounced the clever school

----

[6] Edith Crane letter of November 19, 1922. Thomas Beer had
written Edmund for last-minute data about Stephen for his forth-
coming *Stephen Crane* (1923), and Edith replied because her father
had died the previous month, on September 20th. The Beer-Edith
Crane letters, once in the Alfred A. Knopf files, have been in my files
since 1952, the gift of Editor Herbert Weinstock.

in literature. It seemed to me that there must be something more in life than to sit and cudgel one's brains for clever and witty expedients. So I developed all alone a little creed of art which I thought was a good one. Later I discovered that my creed was identical with the one of Howells and Garland. . . .

In fact, however, he had not developed "all alone" his little creed of art since it derived from Hamlin Garland's Seaside Assembly lectures at Avon in 1891 and 1892. (Garland recast them in his *Crumbling Idols*, 1894.) "If I had kept to my clever Rudyard-Kipling style, the road might have been shorter, but, ah, it wouldn't be the true road."

Kipling's clever style shows up in Crane's "Four Men in a Cave":

They slid in a body down over the slippery, slimy floor of the passage. The stone avenue must have wibble-wobbled with the rush of this ball of tangled men and strangled cries. The torches went out with the combined assault upon the little man. The adventurers whirled to the unknown in darkness. The little man felt that he was pitching to death, but even in his convolutions he bit and scratched at his companions, for he was satisfied that it was their fault. The swirling mass went some twenty feet and lit upon a level dry place in a strong, yellow light of candles. It dissolved and became eyes.

The dissolution of the "mass" into "eyes" (as Joseph Katz points out) is "one of those 'clever and witty expedients' that Crane rejected in forming his artistic creed. And yet, while the glibness is apparent, one perceives also the beginnings of the later, penetrating style."[7]

---

[7] In his Introduction to *Maggie: A Girl of the Streets*, a facsimile edition of the 1893 *Maggie* published at Gainesville, Florida, 1966.

Willis Johnson of the *Tribune* thought Crane's "Four Men in a Cave" among the best things Crane ever wrote. However, Crane himself evidently thought otherwise:

How I wish I had dropped them [the Sullivan County tales] into the wastebasket! They weren't good for anything, and I am heartily ashamed of them now, but every little while someone rakes them up and tells me how much pleasure he had from reading them—throws them in my face out of compliment.

However, he did not disparage the Sullivan County tales when in June 1895 he proposed to Copeland and Day of Boston that they publish them: "I have considerable work that is not in the hands of publishers. My favorites are eight little grotesque tales of the woods which I wrote when I was clever. The trouble is that they only sum 10,-000 words and I can make no more." In characteristic pose of diffidence he modestly added: "If you think you can make one of your swell little volumes of 10,000, the tales would gain considerably lengthy abuse no doubt." Next, he wrote Mrs. Lily Brandon Munroe that his Boston publishers of *The Black Riders and Other Lines* (May 1895) wished "to re-print those old Sullivan County tales of mine and there is no one in the world has any copies of them but you. Can you not send them to me? Are you coming north this summer? Let me know, when you send the stories." It is possible that Copeland and Day did not publish the Sullivan County pieces because Crane had no copies of press clippings to submit, since Mrs. Munroe did not respond to his request to return them.

His grotesque and pseudo-spooky Sullivan

County tales hark back to Western tall tales and to
the Poe-like horror tales of Ambrose Bierce. Whereas Poe and Bierce try to incite terror in the reader,
Crane on the contrary deflates the terror supposedly
felt by his comic adventurers and thus debunks
the genre of the horror story. Debunking is the
characteristic Crane note not only in these tales but
also in the grotesqueries of *Maggie* and *The Red
Badge*. There is nothing grotesque or ironic in his
deadly serious sketch "The Snake," where for once
the terror rendered has the impact of engaging the
reader in the experienced thing. It is a little master-
piece of its kind, whereas Bierce's "The Man and
the Snake"—a far-fetched Poe-like horror tale—is
too contrived, too artificial to be plausible. As for
Kipling, Crane was influenced by him again and
again, but I do not see Kipling as any dominant in-
fluence on the Sullivan County tales.

The tales are imaginatively narrated incidents
recast with "tall tale" ingredients not intended to be
after the facts. They are short, but they are not for
that reason necessarily short stories. What distin-
guishes the short story from the sketch is the ingre-
dient of a conflict between two opposing forces or
ideas or conditions. A sketch reports a conflict,
whereas a short story creates it. The overall intent
of the tale "Killing His Bear," which is the first of
our Sullivan County tales *(Tribune,* July 31, 1892),
is quite different from the intent of the sketches,
such as "Bear and Panther" or "The Snake."

In "Killing His Bear" man is confronted by the
challenge of nature, the bear. Or by the snake in the
sketch of that title. Or in "The Open Boat," by the
tides which will not permit the shipwrecked sur-
vivors to risk readily the dangerous surf. In *Mag-*

gie and in "The Blue Hotel" it is the environment that challenges and traps man. But as one critic put it,

> in its most serious form the challenge is embodied in the hero. The entire theme of *The Red Badge of Courage* is Henry Fleming's attempt to reckon with his cowardice under the inexorable circumstances of battle. While the challenge is being presented, all that is malignant in nature seems to combine intently upon the predestined victim, but at the moment of inevitable destruction the tension may inexplicably relax and life return to its ordinary calm appearance. The "little man" feels the mountain steady under his feet and become motionless [in "The Mesmeric Mountain"]; the waves pace peacefully "to and fro in the moonlight" at the end of "The Open Boat." "Well, I 'low it's off, Jack," is the gunman's farewell remark in "The Bride Comes to Yellow Sky," and *The Red Badge* ends with the sun striking through a leaden sky. The trial by ordeal is finished; the customary once more takes command—until the next time.[8]

Crane's portrayal of the little man's terror in "Killing His Bear" prepared for the "psychological portrayal of fear" in Henry Fleming in *The Red Badge,* which he began writing in early 1893 and possibly even in late 1892. In his Sullivan County tales he had practiced for his debunking of that vainglorious raw recruit on the battlefield of Chancellorsville. Exactly like Henry Fleming, the little man in "Killing His Bear" indulges in inflated self-images: "Swift pictures of himself in a thousand attitudes under a thousand combinations of circumstances, killing a thousand bears, passed panoramically through him." Crane concludes the tale with the little man kicking the dead bear and gloating over him and waving his hat "as if he were leading

---

[8] "Kinds of Courage and Realism," London *Times Literary Supplement,* July 9, 1964, pp. 581, 620.

the cheering of thousands. He ran up and kicked the ribs of the bear. Upon his face was the smile of the successful lover."

There is "the bear of fiction" set into contrast with "the bear of reality," and the same contrasted and double point of view informs Crane's sketch of Cooper's Uncas—the falsely glorified legendary hero gets debunked. The same deflated bravado characterizes the poetry and the fiction. Illusions undercut by the real thing shape *George's Mother* (1896) and *Maggie: A Girl of the Streets* (1893).

The glorified Pete arouses Maggie's admiration because of his boastful defiance of the world: "When he said, 'Ah, what d'hell!' his voice was burdened with disdain for the inevitable and contempt for anything that fate might compel him to endure." Constant throughout Crane's writings is the ironic debasement of picturesque fronts. The nameless "little man" of his Sullivan County tales becomes the blustering man of his later fiction.

The Crane hero (to quote James Colvert)[9] creates a flattering image of himself and of the world; whereas in the narrator's ironic viewpoint man is insignificant, "blind to his human weakness and the futility of his actions, pathetically incompetent in the large scheme of things. . . . Trapped within the confining circle of his swelling emotions of self," the hero sees himself

as god-like, dauntless, heroic, the master of his circumstances. The two images mark the extreme boundaries of Crane's imaginative scope—define, as it were, the limits of his vision of the world. For the Crane story again and again interprets the human situation in terms of the ironic tensions created in the contrast between man as he idealizes

---

[9] "Structure and Theme in Stephen Crane's Fiction," *Modern Fiction Studies*, V (Autumn 1959): Stephen Crane Special Number.

himself in his inner thought and emotion *and* man as he actualizes himself in the stress of experience. In the meaning evoked by the ironic projection of the deflated man against the inflated man lies Crane's essential theme: the consequence of false pride, vanity, and blinding delusion.

In that remarkable "Mesmeric Mountain," which is both a Sullivan County tale and a fable, the little man imagines that his ego has been somehow challenged by an imperturbable mountain, and he vows to conquer this obstruction. In spite of being told by his friends that the forest track leads only to Jim Boyd's house, the little man welcomes nature's challenge. When the mountain attacks him, he counter-attacks in a blind fury and finally reaches the top, whereupon he struts as victor. "Immediately he swaggered with valour to the edge of the cliff. His hands were scornfully in his pockets." However, he gains the mountain's top only to find unchanged the world beneath him: " 'Ho!' he said. 'There's Boyd's house and the Lumberland Pike.' " It is plain that Crane intended the imperturbable mountain to be understood symbolically. He ends his fable about the mountain and the little man on this ironic note: "The mountain under his feet was motionless."

"How the Donkey Lifted the Hills" is not a Sullivan County sketch, but as it links thematically with "The Mesmeric Mountain" it is included as companion-piece to that fable and as coda to this collection. Crane's predilection for mountains shaped a good many of his *Black Riders* poems, written before he had seen the mountains of Mexico.

Irving Bacheller, who sent Crane to Mexico in January 1895 to write sketches for his newspaper syndicate, thought "How the Donkey Lifted the Hills" the best thing Crane sent him. It was in-

spired by the mountains Popocatepetl and Iztacci-
huatl, but they are nameless in Crane's fable.

> Many people suppose that the donkey is lazy. This is
> a great mistake. It is his pride.
> Years ago, there was nobody quite so fine as the donkey.
> He was a great swell in those times. No one could express
> an opinion of anything without the donkey showing him
> where he was wrong in it. No one could mention the name
> of an important personage without the donkey declaring
> how well he knew him.
> The donkey was above all things a proud and aristo-
> cratic beast.

And so was Stephen Crane. At Claverack College he
was a great swell, a martinet on the drill field; and
at Syracuse he had few intimate friends because of
his arrogance, his social diffidence. He was a cool
cat, in modern lingo, but otherwise he was unim-
pressive. Having met Hamlin Garland, William
Dean Howells, Elbert Hubbard, and other literary
greats (including Richard Harding Davis and Mark
Twain), "No one could express an opinion of anything without the donkey showing him where he
was wrong in it. No one could mention the name of
an important personage without the donkey declaring how well he knew him." Also, in his pride and
ambition Crane, who toiled and never rested, saw
himself as an ass. As for the legend of the donkey as
lazy, Crane wrote Peaslee, who published a list of his
published works into 1896, "When I look back on
this array, it appears that I have worked, but as a
matter of truth I am very lazy, hating work and only
taking up a pen when circumstances drive me."

A REVIEWER of the 1949 edition of *The Sullivan
County Sketches of Stephen Crane* claimed that al-

most every one of them "is at least in part a study in the transcription of terror."[10] However, not all of the Sullivan County pieces have to do with terror. Courage dominates several of the sketches, including "Hunting Wild Hogs" and "The Last of the Mohicans." In some of the tales (as distinguished from sketches) cowardice and bravado are intermixed, as in "A Tent in Agony." Anything which blends opposites automatically debunks both.

Very interesting are the five new hunting sketches, reproduced here for the first time, and the recently discovered "Last of the Mohicans." Intrinsically many of the Sullivan County pieces are slight things; some of the tales are rather pointless. The best of the tales is "The Holler Tree." The best of the sketches is "The Snake." Splendid are the fables "The Mesmeric Mountain" and "How the Donkey Lifted the Hills."

The Sullivan County Tales and Sketches ask for and reward our reappraisal of the evolution of Crane's genius. They contain the seeds of themes that sprouted almost simultaneously in the grotesqueries of *Maggie* and *The Red Badge,* wherein he rapidly developed his gift for the psychological probing of character and related scene. They contain the seeds of his painterly and impressionistic style with its addiction to color adjectives, metaphor, and symbol. William Dean Howells rightly remarked of the author of *Maggie* in 1893: "Here is a writer who has sprung into life fully armed."

R. W. STALLMAN

Storrs, Connecticut
27 September, 1967

[10] Herbert Barrows, "Sketches in Terror," New York *Times Book Review,* May 8, 1949.

Thomas Beer in his *Stephen Crane* (New York, 1923) finds fear to be the motivating obsession of Crane's life and works. In theme and style, Berryman's *Stephen Crane* is Beer all over again.

The Tales and Sketches

THE LAST OF THE MOHICANS

HIS ASPECT IN FICTION CONTRADICTED
BY HIS FAME IN FOLK-LORE

HARTWOOD, *Sullivan County, N.Y.,* Feb.
15.—Few of the old, gnarled and weather-
beaten inhabitants of the pines and boulders
of Sullivan County are great readers of books
or students of literature. On the contrary,
the man who subscribes for the county's
weekly newspaper is the man who has attained
sufficient position to enable him to leave his
farm labors for literary pursuits. The historical traditions of the region have been handed
down from generation to generation, at the
firesides in the old homesteads. The aged
grandsire recites legends to his grandson; and
when the grandson's head is silvered he takes
his corn-cob pipe from his mouth and trans-
fixes his children and his children's children
with stirring tales of hunter's exploit and Indian battle. Historians are wary of this form
of procedure. Insignificant facts, told from
mouth to mouth down the years, have been
known to become of positively appalling importance by the time they have passed from
behind the last corn-cob in the last chimney
corner. Nevertheless, most of these fireside
stories are verified by books written by
learned men who have dived into piles of

First reprinted in "Stephen Crane and Cooper's
Uncas," by R. W. Stallman, *American Literature,* 39 (November 1957), pp. 392–96.

mouldy documents and dusty chronicles to establish their facts.

This gives the great Sullivan County thunderbolt immense weight. And they hurl it at no less a head than that which once evolved from its inner recesses the famous Leatherstocking Tales. The old story tellers of this district are continually shaking metaphorical fists at "The Last of the Mohicans" of J. Fenimore Cooper. Tell them that they are aiming their shafts at one of the standard novels of American literature and they scornfully sneer; endeavor to oppose them with the intricacies of Indian history and they shriek defiance. No consideration for the author, the literature or the readers can stay their hands, and they claim without reservation that the last of the Mohicans, the real and only authentic last of the Mohicans, was a demoralized, dilapidated inhabitant of Sullivan County.

The work in question is of course a visionary tale, and the historical value of the plot is not a question of importance. But when the two heroes of Sullivan County and J. Fenimore Cooper, respectively, are compared, the pathos lies in the contrast, and the lover of the noble and fictional Uncas is overcome with great sadness. Even as Cooper claims that his Uncas was the last of the children of the Turtle, so do the sages of Sullivan County roar from out their rockbound fastnesses that their nondescript Indian was the last of the children of the Turtle. The pathos lies in the contrast between the noble savage of fiction and the sworn-to claimant of Sullivan County.

All know well the character of Cooper's hero, Uncas, that bronze god in a North American wilderness, that warrior with the eye of the eagle, the ear of the fox, the tread of the cat-like panther, and the tongue of the wise serpent of fable. Over his dead body a warrior cries:

"Why has thou left us, pride of the Wapanachki? Thy time has been like that of the sun when in the trees; thy glory brighter than his light at noonday. Thou art gone, youthful warrior, but a hundred Wyandots are clearing the briers from thy path to the world of spirits. Who that saw thee in battle would believe that thou couldst die? Who before thee has ever shown Uttawa the way into the fight? Thy feet were like the wings of eagles; thine arm heavier than falling branches from the pine; and thy voice like the Manitto when he speaks in the clouds. The tongue of Uttawa is weak and his heart exceedingly heavy. Pride of the Wapanachki, why hast thou left us?"

The last of the Mohicans supported by Sullivan County is a totally different character. They have forgotten his name. From their description of him he was no warrior who yearned after the blood of his enemies as the hart panteth for the water-brooks; on the contrary he developed a craving for the rum of the white men which rose superior to all other anxieties. He had the emblematic Turtle tattooed somewhere under his shirt-front. Arrayed in tattered, torn and ragged garments which some white man had thrown off, he wandered listlessly from village to village and from house to house, his only ambition being to beg, borrow, or steal a drink.

The settlers helped him because they knew his story. They knew of the long line of mighty sachems sleeping under the pines of the mountains. He was a veritable "poor Indian." He dragged through his wretched life in helpless misery. No one could be more alone in the world than he, and when he died there was no one to call him pride of anything nor to inquire why he had left them.

HUNTING WILD HOGS

Imported Game in Sullivan County

THE ANIMALS ESCAPED FROM A PRIVATE
PARK—ONE OF THEM WOUNDED LEADS
ITS PURSUERS A CHASE OF TWO
HUNDRED MILES—A RARE FORM
OF SPORT IN THE UNITED STATES

HARTWOOD, *Sullivan County, N.Y.,* Feb.
24.—If the well-worn and faded ghost of
many an old scout or trapper of long ago
could arise from beneath the decayed shingle
with awkward hunting-knife carvings where
it lies, it could doubtless create a thrill by re-
citing tales of the panther's gleaming eyes
and sharp claws. Mayhap, in a thousand vari-
eties of chimney-corner, old, gnarled and
knotted forty-niners curdle the blood and
raise the hair of their listeners with legends of
the ferocious and haughty grizzly bear. But
it is certain that there are only three men in
the United States today who have proper
right to thrill anybody, curdle any blood, or
raise any hair with tales of the hunting and
killing of the famous wild hogs of ancient and
modern Europe upon the territory of the
United States. The hog of commerce and
domesticity has escaped from broken pens
and wrecked trains and lives in the wilds of
Canada and Mississippi, and also, it is
claimed, in some parts of this State, but they

make no such sport as the long-haired, swift-running, powerful animals from Europe. The latter are prominent indeed in mythology and history. They are said to be the most wily and cunning of animals. They are very fleet of foot and make great speed through exceedingly rough country. The Sullivan County hunters say that when one of these animals "strikes a line" for a certain point they will not stop for obstructions that would make a bear turn out. They say that they have seen bunches of scruboaks as big as a man's wrist broken and bent aside like reeds where one of the wild hogs has charged through them. They turn out for no bush or little tree, but bolt directly at it. In the fields they root holes with their snouts that would flatter a plough.

Otto Plock, a wealthy New York banker, has a country-seat in the Neversink Valley. He imported a number of wild hogs from Europe and turned them loose in his park. The shaggy beasts must have added a picturesqueness to Mr. Plock's grounds. But one morning they disappeared. They digged under the fences with their strong snouts and scattered over the country. They almost immediately began a series of night expeditions against the farmers' corn and potato fields. It is said that they did great damage. In a single night they would so root up a field with their powerful hoofs and snouts that it would be unrecognizable the next day. The farmers became agitated. They were aroused to action. They turned out in armed brigades. They spent certain sums for ammunition. In the corner stores they laid their plans, and individuals told what they were going to do. They then mustered their forces and attacked the surrounding hills. The wild hogs evaded the army with astonishing ease. The farmers then turned their attention to poison. They fixed up little meals and left them in open places but with no success. To one farm the hogs took a great liking. In its corn-fields they even tore down stalks by the dozen and heaped them in a fence-corner to sleep upon. A neighbor decided to make an investigation. He took a boy, a gun and a position behind a wall, and sat waiting one night for the appearance of the hogs. But he went to sleep. Then the boy, looking over the wall, discovered the wild hogs, not fifteen feet away. He cried out and the animals ran. The man groaned, grunted, stood up, rubbed his eyes, remembered about the hogs, and shot off his gun. The hogs went on. Later the skeleton of the wild boar was found on Shawangunk Mountain. The tusks were about eight inches in length.

The great liar appeared all over Orange and Sullivan Counties, and lots of wild hogs were seen. Children going to school were frightened home by wild hogs. Men coming home late at night saw wild hogs. It became a sort of fashion to see wild hogs and turn around and come back. But when the outraged farmers made such a terrific onslaught upon the stern and rock-bound land, the wild hogs, it appears, withdrew to Sullivan County. This county may have been formed by a very reckless and distracted giant who, observing the tract of tipped-up and impossible ground, stood off and carelessly pelted trees and boulders at it. Not admiring the results of his labors he set off several earthquakes under it and tried to wreck it. He succeeded beyond his utmost expectations, undoubtedly. In the holes and crevices, valleys and hills, caves and swamps of this uneven country, the big game of the southern part of this State have made their last stand. Isolated wanderers are sometimes chased by everybody who owns a gun, and by every dog that has legs, in thickly-populated portions of other counties, but here is where the bear tears the bark from the pines, devoid of the fear of hunters until he hears the yelp of the hounds on the ridges.

Here the wild hogs were in a country which just suited them. Its tangled forests, tumbled rocks and intricate swamps were for them admirable places of residence. Here they remained unmolested for a long time. The first man to kill one of them was Special County Judge William H. Crane, of Port Jervis. While on one of the Hartwood Park hunts, he was standing on a "runway" for deer. He suddenly heard a great scampering of feet and crackling of brush ahead and to the right of him. The next moment a small herd of what afterward proved to be the wild hogs dashed through the brush to his right. Turning quickly, he caught a glimpse of a brown body and fired. They carried home a wild hog weighing 200 pounds. The carcass was inspected, photographed and sketched. A magnificent skin, with stuffed head, now hangs in the clubhouse at Hartwood Park.

The last hog hunt resulted in untold glory and meat for the successful ones. Lew

Boyd, the famous bear hunter, was the hero
of the expedition. He is a six-foot-four-inch
man, with broad shoulders, a good eye, and
legs that have no superior for travel in a
rough country. He chased one of the hogs
in this hunt for over 200 miles, and the animal was shot by him on the seventh day of
the chase. A party of hunters took the trail of
two of the hogs and followed it for two days.
They did not catch sight of the game. On
the third day they met Lew Boyd. He joined
them, and they followed the trails in the
snow all day. Toward night, one by one, the
party began to be discouraged and to drop
out. Finally all had disappeared over the
ridges but Boyd, who never disappears in
such case, and Charles Stearns, of Oakland
Valley. They plodded along together, endeavoring to get over a few miles more before sunset. As they were passing through a
little gulch, Boyd, upon looking up the side
of it, perceived both wild hogs in the bushes
about 100 yards away. As he exclaimed to
his companion, one of the hogs wheeled and
tore through the bushes like a brown cy-
clone. Boyd whirled about and fired, but the
animal did not stop. The other one came
charging down the hill directly at the hunters.
Stearns fired within forty yards, and that hog,
too, then wheeled and scurried over the hill
after her companion. The hunters followed
as rapidly as possible. Some 400 yards from
the scene of the shooting Boyd suddenly discovered that in their great haste they were
following but one track. They turned back,
and found where the two animals had separated. Following the new track they came to a

dead hog in the brush. Stearns of course argued that this was his game. Boyd then went on after the other. Along the trail were great clots of blood from a wound in the throat. Yet the hog travelled with great speed, and Boyd was compelled to go home that night and leave his hog in the woods. The next day seven men turned out to assist in the search. The party trailed the wounded animal to White Cedar Swamp, a narrow, heavily-wooded marsh five miles in length. At the southern end Boyd placed three men on each side of the swamp. These, with two men to drive straight through, would form a very effective pocket. They were ordered to keep about seventy-five yards apart, and not to get behind or ahead, but to proceed slowly and all to keep their relative positions. In this manner Boyd was sure that he could get the hog. This was thought to be a sure mode of procedure, but the second man on the left pushed close to the first man on the same side and the hog passed out at railway speed between the second man and the third man.

They traced the animal to Beaver Dam Swamp and gave up the search for the night. In the morning they met near the place and Boyd placed his men about the swamp. There was a young man with a bulldog upon the scene who said his dog would fight anything. Boyd told him, however, to hold the animal until the hunters were in their positions, but the young man succeeded with great difficulty in making the bulldog follow the track into the swamps some moments before he should have done so. As a result the hog escaped

from the swamp, and Boyd sent the young
man and his bulldog a safe distance to the
rear. They followed the trail all the rest of
that day. The hog's wound had ceased to
bleed and it was making good time on its
travels. The hunters could only count upon
coming up with it once a day. At night it
would make itself a bed by tearing down
young trees and bushes and heaping them in
a huge pile. Boyd says he has seen a quarter
of an acre pretty well cleared of small growth
to make one of these temporary couches.
When once aroused the hog was good for a
twenty-mile run over the rocks and fallen
logs. The principal hunter had almost an entirely new lot of followers every day. Men
would grow enthusiastic for twenty-four
hours and join the hunt, and drop out next
day to make room for some one else. Some
were frozen away, some were wearied quickly
and a number were scared away. Every night,
except one or two, Boyd returned to his
home from where he left the trail, always at
least six miles away. In the morning he would
walk back and resume it. On the fourth day
the pursuers again were up with the hog,
which had as before hidden itself in a swamp.
Boyd placed his men and had the swamp
beaten. Now, as above mentioned, some of
these men thought the wild hog was a dangerous animal. In such cases men have great
fancies for each other's society, and pairs of
Boyd's men often feebly insisted upon being
allowed to sit upon the same log. As the
swamp was beaten one of the hunters became
lonesome and went over to see another
hunter. The other hunter came half way to

meet the first hunter. The hog left the swamp six feet from where the first hunter was told to stand. Boyd was angry. Three times had he laid careful plans and three times had a man who was in a hurry, a man with a bull-dog and a man who was lonesome made all his efforts vain. He called the lonesome men and stated the case in forcible English, con-cluding with the remark: "Boys, if you are frightened, go home! Don't come into the woods and hunt an animal you are afraid of." The young men tilted their noses, shouldered their weapons and made large and defiant tracks in the snow over the hill.

The chase continued all that day and all the next. At the close of the fifth all the hunters gave up the hunt except Boyd. They told him they were rapidly freezing to death, they were worn to skin and bone, and they could not keep up any longer. Boyd called them several names, but they were firm. They departed after impressing upon him the fact that he was doomed to certain death from cold, exposure or fatigue if he did not give up the hunt. In reply he hitched up his trousers and started on his lonely quest.

The hog now showed the first signs of giving out. It did not stop any more to make those elaborate preparations for a night of repose, but simply crawled under a slanting rock or fallen tree as if it had no time to spare. The fifth night was spent by Boyd in Oakland. There they tried to dissuade him. They told him he would never catch it, and if he did it would kill him. An old German told him frightful tales of the animal's pow-ers in battle. He told how horses and men went down before the terrible tusk of the boar of Europe and Bengal. He said that in his native land the wild hogs used often to tip the bark from the pines, rub the pitch into their bristles and then go and roll in a soft clay, which, baked upon their sides by the sun, would make them impervious to bullets. Boyd failed to be impressed. The sixth day was a long and cold one. An icy north wind swept over the ridges and through the gulleys, and the snow drifted heavily. Long icicles hung on Boyd's mustache and his face was frozen blue as he clambered over logs, fell down rocks and plunged through snowbanks, the while keeping both eyes upon the tracks of the hog, which were rapidly being obliterated by the snow. The close of the day brought him no success.

The next day he again took up the chase. The drifting snow made the task of keeping the trail a difficult one. Several times he found himself off the track and lost time looking it up. About noon he discovered fresh blood. This made him, of course, redouble his exertions. Late in the day he discovered a fox standing in the track of the hog, sniffing at the blood on the snow. He fired at the fox and hit it behind the ear. Immediately after the report there was a grunt in the bushes twenty yards away; the wild hog bounded from a clump of bushes and swiftly plunged through the woods. Instantly Boyd turned and fired. Then he started on a run in pursuit. A hundred yards further on he found the hog lying stone dead. Half an hour later it would have been too dark to have shot correctly. He left the dead hog and walked eight miles in the dark through the woods and drifts to his home. In the morning he drove his team upon old logging roads to within a mile or so of his game. Then he and a boy tied a stick in its jaws and dragged it over the stone to the horses. On the afternoon of the eighth day the carcass was hung up in his barn and the struggle was over. Assuming that only five of the wild hogs were in Mr. Plock's park and escaped, the Hartwood Park hunters have accounted for all of them but one. Judge Crane took a second shot in the direction of the fast-lessening noise, after he had fired at the spot of brown in the brush, and it is believed by Boyd that a second pig received a fatal wound from that shot. This of course would end the hunting of the wild hog in the United States.

The people of Sullivan County are wonderful yarn-spinners and they have some great additions to their list of tales. Doubtless for years to come those that know the story will tell to admiring listeners how "Lew" Boyd chased the wounded wild hog for 200 miles.

THE LAST PANTHER

An Ancient Memory of Sullivan County

HARTWOOD PARK, *N.Y.*, March 26 *(Special).*—So far as known, the last of the panthers which once were plentiful in this part of the country was killed in 1820 by a Negro who, flushed with victory and panting with pride, received from the hands of the admiring authorities, in the presence of his friends, filled with sympathetic joy at his good fortune, the munificent reward of $15. In the old days entangled, disordered and intricate Sullivan County was the home of dozens of these animals. They, of course, were accounted to be more formidable and more dangerous than any of the other animals of the swamps and ridges. They frequently made depredations upon the cattle and sheep and sometimes attacked men. The settlers are said to have believed that the panthers would sometimes imitate the cries of children and thus lure victims away from the houses and to the woods. But, although the memories of the old inhabitants bristle with tales of battles with panthers, the tales contain no specific accounts of the panther's siren voice.

43

They tell how individuals returning home late on moonless nights ran several miles in great haste and a cold perspiration upon hearing that wild, weird cry ring out, as if a woman were being murdered by a red-handed villain with a knife. But, either because of goods roads or great speed, none of these men seems ever to have been caught. It is evident, too, that they spoke truly, for these hard-working, industrious mountaineers would never run four miles simply to receive nothing at the end but a soulful welcome and a chance to tell a thrilling story. And, in their gentle innocence and guilelessness, they have not the consummate art of the actor of lurid drama, who rushes upon the stage from a point six feet from the edge of the wing and, sinking down, pantingly cries that he has been pursued eighteen miles by a band of Indians. So it is apparent that travelling by night was once a dangerous practice in Sullivan County.

There were many stout-hearted and quick-shooting hunters in the region who used to like nothing better than a "brush with a painter." But it was difficult to get a good dog to follow the track. Most dogs, upon smelling a panther trail, would shrivel up and quake or mayhap howl in a distressing manner. But there were a few Sullivan County dogs who, confident of their own ability, would not hesitate to worry the retreating form of a man-eating tiger. These dogs were at a premium, although even they, when approaching a panther, would give mournful tone to their howl.

Nelson Crocker, long since dead, is said to have seen seven panthers at once, a feat which probably surpasses the wildest dream of the most able and proficient delirium-tremens expert in the country. Crocker was hunting in "Painter Swamp" one day when he discovered the tracks of a number of panthers. His dog was a good one, and briskly followed the trail. At noon, the hunter sat down on a log to eat his luncheon. As he slowly put the last morsel in his mouth there was a chorus of howls from the surrounding bushes, and he saw seven panthers in rapid succession. He fired at one and killed it, while his dog was soundly thrashed by another. Crocker quickly decided that the sooner he emerged from the swamp the better, so he retreated, preceded by a very willing dog. The next day he went back to skin his game and recover his hat, which he had lost. After shooting a second panther, he and his dog were again forced to retreat by a third. This time, to accelerate his speed, he was forced to throw away his rifle. Having safely arrived on high ground, he decided to return for his weapon. He recovered it, and after a three-handed fight, in which he lost part of his dog, he killed a third panther. He skinned all three and proceeded joyously homeward.

Cyrus Dodge, down the dim vista of rural history, follows close with six panthers the shade of Nelson Crocker. At Long Pond he saw six panthers at once. He ran out into the pond and, standing in the water up to his waist, shot four of them.

An old authority on hunting claims that a man by the name of Calvin Bush was the prince of panther-killers. Bush was a clear-headed, nervous-limbed, muscular hunter, who was as good for his inches as any man in the county. He had a dog that was nearly as famous as himself. He had many adventures with the animals, and killed a large number of them. It is said that once, when he and a friend were hunting together, they shot and wounded a panther which took refuge in the top of a tall tree. Bush remarked to his companion: "I'm going to have some fun with that beast." He then cut a pole and climbed a tree close to the one in which the panther crouched. Straddling a limb, and twining his legs to preserve his balance, the hunter poked the wounded animal in the ribs until, enraged and furious, it fell to the ground in an ineffectual attempt to spring upon its assailant. There it was dispatched by the other man. On that hunt of two days they killed five panthers.

Upon one occasion a wounded animal sprang at the hunter's dog. Bush's gun was empty, but he stood by his valorous and faithful canine friend. He aimed a blow at the panther's head with a hatchet. The animal dodged and caught the handle in its teeth. It wrenched the implement from the hunter's hand with the utmost ease, and then dropped it to fight the dog, which had begun a noisy attack in the rear. While the panther was mutilating the dog, Bush loaded his gun and shot it through the head. He always carried a crooked finger, which was made by the panther's teeth when it grasped the hatchet-handle.

The people around Monticello were disturbed by two of these animals which used to prowl around in the night and cry like children. They sent for Bush and his famous "painter-dog." The hunter chased and overtook the animals in a swamp and killed them both.

A score or so of hunters from Callicoon chased a huge panther into its den in a ledge of rocks. They closed up the entrance to the lair and departed, returning on the next day with reinforcements and a determination to kill the dread beast. It had retreated to a dark inner recess. After a council of war, in which every gentleman of the company told the others how to hunt panthers, they decided to place a lighted candle where the rays would gleam down a rifle-barrel. This was done and a man ventured in until he perceived the inevitable "fiery eyeballs." Then he pulled [the] trigger. The report was followed by howls from the wounded animal, which caused a retreat of the entire army. That which a moment before had been the scene of a well-planned campaign turned to one of the wildest confusion and disorder. Four hundred yards from the scene of the attack the little band rallied, and it was then perceived that nearly every member had been wounded. Bruised shins, lacerated feet and skinned elbows were plentiful as a result of the wild charge over rocks and logs and through brambles. One brave man had bumped his head on a rock right where the panther had once walked. Slowly they again approached the den wherein lurked the foe. It was necessary that every precaution be taken or they might be attacked in overwhelming numbers. They arrived safely with no accident. Anther man ventured in and cracked away at the "fiery eyeballs" with the same result as before, excepting that the panther howled less and the army did not retreat quite so far. A third man followed and with his bullet prostrated the beast upon the floor of the den, where it roared so faintly that the army almost refused to retreat at all. The leading spirits then grappled with the question as to how to get the animal out. It had retreated so far back in the cave that it was possible only for a boy to get to it. A boy volunteered, took off his coat in the presence of his admiring friends, went in and came out again, making a remark irrelevant to the subject, about the weather, which none heeded. A small lad who had not figured very highly in the retreats owing to his short legs and boyish strength proceeded to pile his coat, vest and hat behind a bush, and then sneaked into the cave armed with a Spanish dirk and hatchet. Through the dark and uneven passage he crept until he could see the yellow-green eyes of the wounded animal staring at him fixedly. Nearer he crawled until he could hear its slow, labored breathing and could see it evidently gathering its forces for a last desperate effort. Reaching forward, the lad sunk his hatchet-blade in the beast's skull, and as it writhed and struggled on the floor in its death agony he cut its throat with his dirk. When the animal's limbs gave their last convulsive quivers he seized it and dragged it forth into the presence of the army, who thereupon cheered and went home and told about the killing of the panther.

SULLIVAN COUNTY BEARS

HARTWOOD PARK, *N.Y.*, April 18.—Old settlers say that there are more bears in Sullivan County today than there were a generation ago. A number of facts make this statement one easy to be believed. Long ago the forests thronged with a race of brawny hunters who shouldered deadly rifles and were keen-eyed for the chase. The hills were dotted with the little homes and clearings of woodsmen who made their living with axes, were iron-nerved and clear-eyed, and could shoot true. Tanneries and sawmills giving employment to many men sat by the sides of all the streams. The woods were full of the sounds of axe-blows and the creakings of ox-chains. Youths grew up with desire for fame, and they took rifles and went to seek it in the woods. A hardy race of huntsmen made terrible war on the game. With the vanishing of the great forests these men disappeared from the face of the earth. Not all men now are hunters. There are those surrounded by the best cover for game who never taste partridge or venison the year round.

When Sullivan County was covered with a growth of heavy forest-trees, hunters walking through the woods had good travelling and could see far, for the brush, under the shade of the great trees, was not thick. Now the huge forest monarchs have gone their ways to the river-rafts and the sawmills, and after them have come second-growth and brush, thick as the hair on a dog's back. The game finds excellent crouching places in the dense thickets, and escapes the hunter's eye with ease.

Contrary to general belief, the shyest of all the animals which naturally live in these woods is the bear, and not the deer. The oldest hunters of this region assert this fact positively. They say that it is a comparatively easy thing to get a shot at a deer, but a difficult one to get the chance of holding a rifle on a bear as a target. The bear is much keener. If he hears a hunter or hunters coming a quarter of a mile away he will immediately get up and dust, and the hunter may not find out that he has been in the vicinity at all. The old bears, however, are not inclined to be very shy. They grow confident in their own strength and prowess, and do not always flinch when they accidentally meet a human being. For instance, if one of these old warriors should happen to be confronted by a man when crossing the road, he would stop and look, with curiosity expressed in his eyes, and maybe snarl and show his teeth if the man made a sudden motion. Having satisfied his curiosity he would quietly move off into the brush, generally leaving the man in a limp state.

The bear makes his bed for the winter in a number of different ways. Sometimes he crawls down in a hole, crevice or cave and snuggles under dead leaves and sticks. At other times, when trees fall down and make tangled masses, he crawls in the thickest part.

He has also been known to gather great bunches of laurel boughs and pile them in a great heap; then climb on top and sleep, letting the snow fall right on him. When the bear is engaged in making his couch he makes a pile of brush six or eight feet in diameter and three or four feet high. He will often strip a young tree so bare of leaf and branch that it looks like a flagpole, with only a small tassel on top. In the summer he has a private bath. He goes to some swamp and with his strong claws digs down into the black mud until he has hollowed out a little place which soon filters full of a black ooze. Here the bear lies and wallows through the dead heat of a summer's day in the forest, when not a leaf in the woods stirs and the earth and the animals on it bake and swelter. Beaten paths are generally found to lead to each one of these, showing that the bear loves his slimy baths above all things.

He takes care of his claws in the same manner in which a cat does. Scarred trees can be found in the wilds, showing that the bears stand up on their hind legs and claw down the bark.

In the spring and early summer the bears live on roots and sprouts and tender leaves, together with the grubs and worms which they get by turning over the stones in the valleys. Boulders too heavy for a man to lift are found rolled recklessly about by bears in pursuit of grubs. Of course when a bear finds a bee tree he is a happy animal. In the late summer and fall he resorts to the berry patches and scruboak ridges and feasts on berries and acorns.

But when he first comes out in the spring

he is very hungry and will eat anything he can get. He will dine on dead horse, or will steal a pig from a pen or a calf from a stable. But when other food is plentiful the black bear will never touch flesh. Hunger will drive him to it, but of his own free will he prefers a diet of vegetables.

A bear hunt in this region is in reality a chase from swamp to swamp. The bear, when hunted, always runs to a swamp and hides in the thickest most inaccessible part. Here he will stay until driven out by the approach of a man or a dog on the trail. The hunters always do what they call "surrounding" the swamp, although, of course, they do not really do so, owing to the size of the swamp and the limit to the number of men. Then the guide and the dogs generally follow in on the trail, after leaving the rest of the party stationed at convenient points on the outskirts. The best spot to get a shot at a bear is at the place where he entered the swamp, for he is pretty sure to come out there. But he is a wary strategist. He crouches in the depths of a log maybe and listens. He hears voices off to the north, as the hunters take up their positions on the "runways" in that direction. From the east come the faint sounds of the snapping of a twig as a hunter makes room for the better sweep of his rifle barrel. To the south he may hear a man cautiously scramble up on a log or an old stump, and in the rear he hears faintly the whines of the hound on a warm trail and the low, directing voice of the guide. The hunters may be a long distance away, but the old bear hears them and interprets the sounds and lays his plans accordingly. He shows ability and skill in his effort to come unscathed from the tight place he is in. He runs some distance and then stops, perhaps, and listens intently. Maybe his ears tell him to take a new direction, and he starts rapidly off. Whether he gets out of the swamp now or not depends entirely upon what backwoods general has stationed the men, and who the men are. Even if they are expert shots, it will avail them nought unless they are placed by a leader who knows the important posts, who can calculate on the bear's conclusions and guard against errors of judgment. To be a strategist equal to emergencies which arise when hunting in Sullivan County takes a lifetime in the woods, a thirty years'[1] study of the habits of animals.

After that difficulty is overcome there exists the one of shooting the bear. Some men can hit things with a gun and some men can't. So, even if a hunter on a "runway" gets a shot, the bear has a dozen chances to escape. He immediately starts for another swamp three or four miles away. It must not be supposed that he travels slowly. A bear can keep well ahead of a good dog all day, through bushes, swale or any kind of country, except in the open fields. Those animals, which people call awkward and ungainly, run as easily as rabbits. Nor do they "shamble" or "wobble" or "flounder." They have an easy, rapid gait, which carries them swiftly and easily away from the pursuing dogs.

Not many dogs will follow bear. Some quake and shiver when they scent the trail.

---

[1] Text has: yars'.

Some will run an old trail, but will turn back when it freshens. Others will run an old trail with rapidity, but will slow up and run poorly on the fresh scent, giving a mournful "sorry-like" tone to their yelps as they near the bear's possible crouching place. But there are stout-hearted hounds of good breed who will take a bear's track eagerly and run with a determination to overtake the animal. If such a dog comes up with a wounded bear, he will tackle him without a moment's hesitation. A good bear-hound seems to take the trail with a strange vindictiveness and blood-thirstiness. He seems eager for the bear's life and will follow until he is totally exhausted, the bear is killed, or his owner takes him off the scent. Old Scout, the former pride of Hartwood Park and the best bear-runner in Sullivan County, ran the game with the ferocity of a wolf. If he came up with a wounded bear, there ensued immediately a tremendous scuffle. His valiant heart never flinched at the sight of huge, gleaming teeth, nor great, spreading claws, nor at the sound of the fierce snarls. One of his human friends once stood over a whirling chaos of dog's feet and bear's feet and of dog's ears and bear's ears. From it there rose a haze of two different kinds of hair. Snarls and snaps, growls and roars, filled the forests. Soon the mass took shape, and the bear appeared with his forefeet planted on the dog's body, chewing and rending it with teeth and claws. Old Scout never whimpered nor made complaint. The bear left off and started to run away. The hound, gathering his bleeding form together, gave furious pursuit. The friend of Old Scout, who had not dared to fire at the mass of dog and bear, then dropped the game with a ball behind the ear. The dog plunged savagely upon the fallen foe, but, finding that there was no more fight in the animal, sat down and contentedly wagged his tail. When a bear is shot through the head, he "falls dead in his tracks." If the bullet happens to break the spinal column, he also then falls dead. But plant a bullet anywhere else, and the animal may run a mile with it in him. Most hunters prefer to aim at a point under the foreshoulder when the bear is moving rapidly through difficult cover. If one hits him there, it is almost certain that the bullet will pierce the heart, pass through the lungs, or sever an artery.

Although no one can doubt the great strength and fighting ability of the bear, yet it is difficult to reconcile the bear of fiction with the bear of reality. The black bear of the hunter's tales was a fighter. He had a fashion of rearing upon his hind legs and crushing men and guns in a passionate embrace. Story books bristle with accounts of his enthusiastic receptions of sportsmen. The books say that when the Indians and black bears roamed these hills, the brave who possessed a necklace of the claws of this terrible animal was considered a great warrior. Save the dreaded panther, the bear was the monarch of the wilds. Indians were generally knocked rudely about when they ventured upon a hand-to-hand encounter with bruin.

The gentlemen who figure in fiction as "scouts" and "guides" and what not are reputed to have stood, attired in fringed bearskin, about the camp-fires and told of desperate attacks upon themselves by ferocious bears. They are supposed to have carried so many scars that their bodies looked like road-maps. But the black bear of today is not a fighter. Of course, when cornered he will make a fight for his life, as a gray squirrel will. A she bear will fight to protect her young. A wounded bear will turn and beat off the dogs. If exasperated in close quarters, a bear may let drive savagely with both paws and snarl and bite with great fierceness. In this case, it is advisable to retire, if convenient. An old bear encountering someone accidentally in the woods will show his teeth. If the man insists on a row he will get a fine one. But the modern black bear is not a fighter by choice. He depends more on his four feet and his keen senses for safety than he does upon his prowess.

THE WAY IN
SULLIVAN COUNTY

A STUDY IN THE EVOLUTION
OF THE HUNTING YARN

FOWLERVILLE, *Sullivan County, N.Y.,*
May 4.—A county famous for its hunting and
its hunters is naturally prolific of liars.
Wherever the wild deer boundeth and the
shaggy bear waddleth, there does the liar
thrive and multiply. Every man cultivates
what taste he has for prevarication lest his
neighbors may look down on him. One can
buy sawlogs from a native and take his word
that the bargain is square, but ask the same
man how many deer he has killed in his
lifetime and he will stop working, take a seat
on the snake-fence and paralyze the questioner with a figure that would look better
than most of the totals to the subscription
lists for monuments to national heroes. The
inhabitants grow up to regard each other with
painful suspicion. So there is very little field
for the expert liars among their fellows. They
must keep to a certain percentage or they
will lose caste, but there is little pleasure in
it for them because everybody knows everybody else. The only real enjoyment is when
the unoffending city man appears. They welcome him with joyful cries. After he recovers from a paroxysm of awe and astonishment he seizes his pen and, with flashing eye
and trembling, eager fingers, writes those

brief but lurid sketches which fascinate and charm the reading public while the virtuous bushwhacker, whittling a stick near by, smiles in his own calm and sweet fashion.

Hence we have the tale of the farmer lad who rounded up the herd of seven bears and drove them to a pasture lot by means of a tin huckleberry pail and an iron nerve. Hence comes also the story of the young man who hitched the team of cubs to a soap-box and trained them to drag him over the snow, with admirable success, until one day when chased by a dog they dragged him and the soap-box up into the top of a tall hemlock. The writer ended his tale at about that point, and so it is an open question whether the young man and the soap-box ever got down from the tree or are up there at this moment. Scores of tales of even more brilliancy than the two recited are prevalent.

It is inevitable that this should be the state of society in Sullivan County as well as in Pike County, and the vicinity of Scranton, Penn. In a shooting country, no man should tell just exactly what he did. He should tell what he would have liked to do or what he expected to do, just as if he accomplished it. And they all take the proper course, bringing the bump of creative genius up to a high point of development and adding little legends to the hunting lore of the region, which will undoubtedly go down the ages and impress coming generations with the fact that the Sullivan County bushwhackers were very great men indeed. Only two tales need be introduced to illustrate the lines of thought followed by these able and proficient gentlemen—one of great execution done by the liar, the other in which the liar figures as one who saw great things. Quite a number of men sometimes tell the same tale as part of their own individual experience. For instance, six men say that once when they, or he, was on a hunt, he was crawling cautiously through a thicket toward a huge fallen tree. Suddenly when he was some yards distant a bear raised its head over the log and peered at him. He aimed at it and fired. The bear disappeared behind the log. The hunter proceeded toward the log, when he saw the bear's head again. He fired and the head disappeared as before. He crawled on, when for the third time he perceived the bear's head. He fired again. Upon crawling to the log and looking over he found three dead bears.

Once upon a time two men slept all night in a cave. Upon waking up and peering out in the morning they perceived a huge bear and a panther some distance away. The animals were about forty yards apart. The bear was eating huckleberries from the bushes, while the panther was sharpening its claws on a tree like a cat. The men according to an agreement fired simultaneously, one at the bear and one at the other animal. There came a roar of astonishment from the bear and a snarl of surprise from the panther. Gazing around, they perceived each other, and each decided that the other animal was the cause of its sudden pain. Filled with anger they furiously fell upon each other, bent on taking full revenge. They both seemed overcome with indignation at the insult offered them. They roared and snarled and fought furiously. Brown hair and tawny fur flew about in handfuls, and blood stained the stones. In the frantic fight, it was impossible to tell which was getting the better of it, so the brilliant-minded and philosophical hunters dangled their heels and smilingly looked on until the panther finished the bear. Then they shot the victor.

BEAR AND PANTHER

VENGEANCE FOR THE WRONGS
TO A KITTEN[1]

HARTWOOD, *N.Y.*, July 12.—Two or three
men known individually as positively the oldest inhabitants of the county can tell stories
of the time when the panthers used to haunt
these woods and make desperate hunting. A
story of a disturbance between a bear and a
panther is their favorite, and as each oldest
inhabitant insists upon telling it whenever a
listener heaves in sight, it may be said to be
well authenticated.

Two young men in passing near a ledge
while out upon a deer hunt discovered the
entrance to a cave. Before it on the ground
were the bones of a deer and other animals.
Tracks made by a panther were plentiful.
They concealed themselves a short distance
away behind a fallen log and waited for the
animal to either approach the cave or emerge
from it.

Soon they heard a great grunting and
puffing, accompanied by squeals and squeaks,
down in the cave. The agitated hunters made
ready and drew beads on the mouth of the
cave. A big bear clambered slowly out and
sat down on the ground before the cave. One
hunter was about to shoot from his ambush
when the other man restrained him, for he
had observed that the bear had a little pan-

---

[1] Text has: *of* a Kitten.

ther kitten in his mouth. The hunters then remained quietly in concealment and watched the proceedings.

The bear with a crunch of his jaws squeezed the little panther to death and then threw it out upon the ground. Perched upon his quarters, solemn and dignified, he watched the last writhings of the little panther with all the gravity of demeanor and close attention of a scientific investigator. When the little animal ceased struggling, he tapped it softly with his paw and seemed to be endeavoring to get it to wriggle some more. But as the kitten lay motionless and stiff, he turned about and waddled rather painfully through the aperture into the cave. There was a renewal of the gruntings and puffings, squealings and squeakings within the cave, and after a short time the bear reappeared with another kitten in his mouth. The first scene was repeated. The bear, after remaining an interested spectator of the second little panther's last agonies, disappeared again within the cave and brought the third small victim. This one, however, seizing a moment when the pressure of the bear's jaws lessened, gave voice to a terrified little scream. It was immediately answered by the blood-curdling roar of the female panther some distance away.

The bear at once dropped the kitten as if in great dismay, and shambled awkwardly about in the most intense excitement and trepidation. The little panther lay on the ground and squealed. It was answered by the roars of its mother as she hurried to the rescue. The bear, now evidently considering that in his eagerness for scientific investigation he had put himself in a bad fix, cast a last despairing look at the open mouth of the kitten, and then started off in a rapid wobble in an opposite direction to the one from which the cries of the "she-painter" proceeded. A moment later a huge panther, with blazing yellow eyes and foam-dripping jaws, bounded into the open space, with every hair bristling on her tawny back, and her lithe limbs quivering and trembling with eagerness. The bear cast one look over his shoulder and made off faster than ever. The panther began an earnest pursuit, and gained rapidly.

The bear, seeing that the panther was overtaking him, hastily ascended a tree. The panther sprang into the lower branches, and in a second had ripped two big bunches of brown hair from the bear's back as that animal, in his terror, climbed the tree with the celerity of a schoolboy. He crawled out on a branch, but the panther followed. The bear was now in extremities. There was but one remedy. So he wound himself up in a brown ball and dropped to the ground. He struck with a sort of smash, unwound himself, and started on a frantic "lope" for safety. But with two or three bounds the panther was down the tree and near to him. She sprang upon the bear, buried her teeth in his throat, and with her powerful claws tore out his entrails. The hunters then shot the panther. They found that the greater part of the bear's hide was literally torn to ribbons.

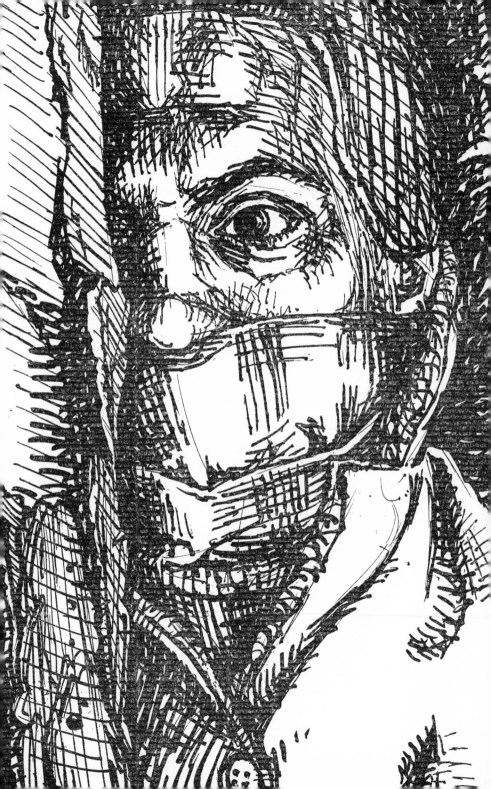

KILLING HIS BEAR

A WINTER TRAGEDY WITH THREE ACTORS

[*No dateline*] In a field of snow some green
pines huddled together and sang in quavers
as the wind whirled among the gullies and
ridges. Icicles dangled from the trees' beards,
and fine dusts of snow lay upon their brows.
On the ridge-top a dismal choir of hemlocks
crooned over one that had fallen. The dying
sun created a dim purple and flame-colored
tumult on the horizon's edge and then sank
until level crimson beams struck the trees. As
the red rays retreated, armies of shadows stole
forward. A gray, ponderous stillness came
heavily in the steps of the sun. A little man
stood under the quavering pines. He was
muffled to the nose in fur and wool, and a
hideous cap was pulled tightly over his ears.
His cold and impatient feet had stamped a
small platform of hard snow beneath him. A
black-barrelled rifle lay in the hollow of his
arm. His eyes, watery from incessant glaring,
swept over the snowfields in front of him.
His body felt dumb and bloodless, and soft
curses came forth and froze on the icy wind.
The shadows crept about his feet until he
was merely a blurred blackness, with keen
eyes.

Off over the ridges, through the tangled
sounds of night, came the yell of a hound on
the trail. It pierced the ears of the little man
and made his blood swim in his veins. His

eyes eagerly plunged at the wall of thickets across the stone field, but he moved not a finger or foot. Save his eyes, he was frozen to a statue. The cry of the hound grew louder and louder, then passed away to a faint yelp, then still louder. At first it had a strange vindictiveness and bloodthirstiness in it. Then it grew mournful as the wailing of a lost thing, as, perhaps, the dog gained on a fleeing bear. A hound, as he nears large game, has the griefs of the world on his shoulders, and his baying tells of the approach of death. He is sorry he came.

The long yells thrilled the little man. His eyes gleamed and grew small and his body stiffened to intense alertness. The trees kept up their crooning, and the light in the west faded to a dull red splash, but the little man's fancy was fixed on the panting, foam-spattered hound, cantering with his hot nose to the ground in the rear of the bear, which runs as easily and as swiftly as a rabbit, through brush, timber, and swale. Swift pictures of himself in a thousand attitudes under a thousand combinations of circumstances, killing a thousand bears, passed panoramically through him.

The yell of the hound grew until it smote the little man like a call to battle. He leaned forward, and the second finger of his right hand played a low, nervous pat-pat on the trigger of his rifle. The baying grew fierce and blood-curdling for a moment, then the dog seemed to turn directly toward the little man, and the notes again grew wailing and mournful. It was a hot trail.

The little man, with nerves tingling and

blood throbbing, remained in the shadows,
like a fantastic bronze figure, with jewelled
eyes swaying sharply in its head. Occasionally
he thought he could hear the branches of the
bushes in front swish together. Then silence
would come again.

The hound breasted the crest of the
ridge, a third of a mile away, and suddenly
his full-toned cry rolled over the tangled
thickets to the little man. The bear must
be very near. The little man kept so still
and listened so tremendously that he could
hear his blood surge in his veins. All at once
he heard a swish-swish in the bushes. His rifle
was at his shoulder and he sighted uncertainly
along the front of the thicket. The swish of
the bushes grew louder. In the rear the
hound was mourning over a warm scent.

The thicket opened and a great bear, in-
distinct and vague in the shadows, bounded
into the little man's view, and came terrifically across the open snowfield. The little
man stood like an image. The bear did not
"shamble" nor "wobble"; there was no awk-
wardness in his gait; he ran like a frightened
kitten. It would be an endless chase for the
lithe-limbed hound in the rear.

On he came, directly toward the little
man. The animal heard only the crying behind him. He knew nothing of the thing
with death in its hands standing motionless in
the shadows before him.

Slowly the little man changed his aim
until it rested where the head of the approaching shadowy mass must be. It was a
wee motion, made with steady nerves and a
soundless swaying of the rifle barrel; but the

bear heard, or saw, and knew. The animal whirled swiftly and started in a new direction with an amazing burst of speed. Its side was toward the little man now. His rifle barrel was searching swiftly over the dark shape. Under the fore-shoulder was the place. A chance to pierce the heart, sever an artery or pass through the lungs. The little man saw swirling fur over his gun barrel. The earth faded to nothing. Only space and the game, the aim and the hunter. Mad emotions, powerful [enough] to rock worlds, hurled through the little man, but did not shake his tiniest nerve.

When the rifle cracked it shook his soul to a profound depth. Creation rocked and the bear stumbled.

The little man sprang forward with a roar. He scrambled hastily in the bear's track. The splash of red, now dim, threw a faint, timid beam of a kindred shade on the snow. The little man bounded in the air.

"Hit!" he yelled, and ran on. Some hundreds of yards forward he came to a dead bear with his nose in the snow. Blood was oozing slowly from a wound under the shoulder, and the snow about was sprinkled with blood. A mad froth lay in the animal's open mouth, and his limbs were twisted from agony.

The little man yelled again and sprang forward, waving his hat as if he were leading the cheering of thousands. He ran up and kicked the ribs of the bear. Upon his face was the smile of the successful lover.

FOUR MEN IN A CAVE

LIKEWISE FOUR QUEENS;
AND A SULLIVAN COUNTY HERMIT

[*No dateline*] The moon rested for a moment on the top of a tall pine on a hill.

The little man was standing in front of the camp-fire making oration to his companions.

"We can tell a great tale when we get back to the city if we investigate this thing," said he, in conclusion.

They were won.

The little man was determined to explore a cave, because its black mouth had gaped at him. The four men took lighted pine-knots and clambered over boulders down a hill. In a thicket on the mountainside lay a little tilted hole. At its side they halted.

"Well?" said the little man.

They fought for last place and the little man was overwhelmed. He tried to struggle from under by crying that if the fat, pudgy man came after, he would be corked. But he finally administered a cursing over his shoulder and crawled into the hole. His companions gingerly followed.

A passage, the floor of damp clay and pebbles, the walls slimy, green-mossed and dripping, sloped downward. In the cave atmosphere the torches became studies in red blaze and black smoke.

71

"Ho!" cried the little man, stifled and bedraggled, "let's go back." His companions were not brave. They were last. The next one to the little man pushed him on, so the little man said sulphurous words and cautiously continued his crawl.

Things that hung seemed to be on the wet, uneven ceiling, ready to drop upon the men's bare necks. Under their hands the clammy floor seemed alive and writhing. When the little man endeavored to stand erect the ceiling forced him down. Knobs and points came out and punched him. His clothes were wet and mud-covered, and his eyes, nearly blinded by smoke, tried to pierce the darkness always before his torch.

"Oh, I say, you fellows, let's go back," cried he. At that moment he caught the gleam of trembling light in the blurred shadows before him.

"Ho!" he said, "here's another way out."

The passage turned abruptly. The little man put one hand around the corner but it touched nothing. He investigated and discovered that the little corridor took a sudden dip down a hill. At the bottom shone a yellow light.

The little man wriggled painfully about and descended, feet in advance. The others followed his plan. All picked their way with anxious care. The traitorous rocks rolled from beneath the little man's feet and roared thunderously below him. Lesser stones, loosened by the men above him, hit him in the back. He gained a seemingly firm foothold and, turning half about, swore redly at his companions for dolts and careless fools.

The pudgy man sat, puffing and perspiring, high in the rear of the procession. The fumes and smoke from four pine-knots were in his blood. Cinders and sparks lay thick in his eyes and hair. The pause of the little man angered him.

"Go on, you fool," he shouted. "Poor, painted man, you are afraid."

"Ho!" said the little man. "Come down here and go on yourself, imbecile!"

The pudgy man vibrated with passion. He leaned downward. "Idiot . . ."

He was interrupted by one of his feet which flew out and crashed into the man in front of and below him. It is not well to quarrel upon a slippery incline when the unknown is below. The fat man, having lost the support of one pillar-like foot, lurched forward. His body smote the next man, who hurtled into the next man. Then they all fell upon the cursing little man.

They slid in a body down over the slippery, slimy floor of the passage. The stone avenue must have wibble-wobbled with the rush of this ball of tangled men and strangled cries. The torches went out with the combined assault upon the little man. The adventurers whirled to the unknown in darkness. The little man felt that he was pitching to death, but even in his convolutions he bit and scratched at his companions, for he was satisfied that it was their fault. The swirling mass went some twenty feet and lit upon a level dry place in a strong, yellow light of candles. It dissolved and became eyes.

The four men lay in a heap upon the floor of a gray chamber. A small fire smouldered in the corner, the smoke disappearing in a crack. In another corner was a bed of faded hemlock boughs and two blankets. Cooking utensils and clothes lay about, with boxes and a barrel.

Of these things the four men took small cognizance. The pudgy man did not curse the little man, nor did the little man swear in the abstract. Eight widened eyes were fixed upon the centre of the room of rocks.

A great gray stone, cut squarely, like an altar, sat in the middle of the floor. Over it burned three candles in swaying tin cups hung from the ceiling. Before it, with what seemed to be a small volume clasped in his yellow fingers, stood a man. He was an infinitely sallow person in the brown checked shirt of the ploughs and cows. The rest of his apparel was boots. A long gray beard dangled from his chin. He fixed glinting, fiery eyes upon the heap of men and remained motionless. Fascinated, their tongues cleaving, their blood cold, they arose to their feet. The gleaming glance of the recluse swept slowly over the group until it found the face of the little man. There it stayed and burned.

The little man shrivelled and crumpled as the dried leaf under the glass.

Finally the recluse slowly, deeply spoke. It was a true voice from a cave, cold, solemn and damp.

"It's your ante," he said.

"What?" said the little man.

The hermit tilted his beard and laughed a laugh that was either the chatter of a banshee in a storm or the rattle of pebbles in a tin box. His visitors' flesh seemed ready to drop from their bones.

They huddled together and cast fearful eyes over their shoulders. They whispered.

"A vampire!" said one.

"A ghoul!" said another.

"A Druid before the sacrifice," murmured another.

"The shade of an Aztec witch doctor," said the little man.

As they looked, the inscrutable's face underwent a change. It became a livid background for his eyes, which blazed at the little man like impassioned carbuncles. His voice arose to a howl of ferocity. "It's your ante!" With a panther-like motion, he draw a long, thin knife and advanced, stooping. Two cadaverous hounds came from nowhere and, scowling and growling, made desperate feints at the little man's legs. His quaking companions pushed him forward.

Tremblingly he put his hand to his pocket.

"How much?" he said, with a shivering look at the knife that glittered.

The carbuncles faded.

"Three dollars," said the hermit, in sepulchral tones which rang against the walls and among the passages, awakening long-dead spirits with voices. The shaking little man took a role of bills from a pocket and placed "three ones" upon the altar-like stone. The recluse looked at the little volume with reverence in his eyes. It was a pack of playing cards.

Under the three swinging candles, upon the altar-like stone, the gray-beard and the agonized little man played at poker. The three other men crouched in a corner and stared with eyes that gleamed with terror. Before them sat the cadaverous hounds, licking their red lips. The candles burned low and began to flicker. The fire in the corner expired.

Finally the game came to a point where the little man laid down his hand and quavered: "I can't call you this time, sir. I'm dead broke."

"What?" shrieked the recluse. "Not call me? Villain! Dastard! Cur! I have four queens, miscreant." His voice grew so mighty that it could not fit his throat. He choked, wrestling with his lungs for a moment. Then the power of his body was concentrated in a word: "Go!"

He pointed a quivering, yellow finger at a wide crack in the rock. The little man threw himself at it with a howl. His erstwhile frozen companions felt their blood throb again. With great bounds they plunged after the little man. A minute of scrambling, falling and pushing brought them to open air. They climbed the distance to their camp in furious springs.

The sky in the east was a lurid yellow. In the west the footprints of departing night lay on the pine trees. In front of their replenished camp fire sat John Willerkins, the guide.

"Hello!" he shouted at their approach. "Be you fellers ready to go deer huntin'?"

Without replying, they stopped and debated among themselves in whispers.

Finally, the pudgy man came forward.

"John," he inquired, "do you know anything peculiar about this cave below here?"

"Yes," said Willerkins at once, "Tom Gardner."

"What?" said the pudgy man.

"Tom Gardner!"

"How's that?"

"Well, you see," said Willerkins slowly, as he took dignified pulls at his pipe, "Tom Gardner was onct a fambly man, who lived in these here parts on a nice leetle farm. He uster go away to the city orften, and one time he got a-gamblin' in one of them there dens. He went ter the dickens right quick then. At last he kum home one time and tol' his folks he had up and sold the farm and all he had in the worl'. His leetle wife, she died then. Tom, he went crazy, and soon after . . ."

The narrative was interrupted by the little man, who became possessed of devils.

"Iwouldn'tgiveacussifhehadleftme'nough moneytogethomeon, thedoggoned, gray-haired redpirate," he shrilled, in a seething sentence. The pudgy man gazed at the little man calmly and sneeringly.

"Oh, well," he said, "we can tell a great tale when we get back to the city after having investigated this thing."

"Go to the devil!" replied the little man.

ACROSS THE COVERED PIT

THE Rev. C. H. Hoovey, D.D. of [Bridgeport *crossed out*] Connecticut, had the grave and reverent look which betokens his profession. To see the gentleman dressed in shining black in his pulpit on Sunday, one could never imagine that the devout preacher of the gospel was one of the most daring cave explorers in this country. Yet all the noted caverns of this country have been visited by him. No cavern looks so gloomy and forbidding but the doctor feels his boyish spirit of adventure seize him, and he longs to tread its dark mysteries and explore its unknown recesses. The unbroken region beyond the mouth of the Covered Pit in Mammoth Cave was a bug-bear to him. To anyone's knowledge, the mass of tangled slippery slabs that was heaped over the mouth of the pit had never been tread on. As authorities had forbidden anyone to cross this dangerous place, its strength had never been tested. It might be strong enough to allow a train of cars to cross it, and again, the weight of a cat might cause the whole mass to tumble to the unknown depth. The doctor had been to the edge of the pit several times. He would look

Reproduced for the first time from the typescript in Edith Crane papers, once belonging to the Bacon Collamore Crane Collection, in "Stephen Crane: Some New Stories (Part III)," edited by R. W. Stallman, *Bulletin of the New York Public Library*, 61 (January 1957). Evidence that Crane was seeking a publisher is that it is marked "A. T. Vance, 1133 Broadway, N.Y. Press Club." The Holograph MS (29 leaves of yellow paper) is in the Barrett Crane Collection, University of Virginia.

at the huge patches of darkness that showed between the slabs which seem to have been thrown loosely over the mouth of the whole by a giant hand, and then glance at the dim outline of a wide tunnel which led along from the other side of the pits.

A wistful look would come into his eyes, as he would wonder about that unknown land. He would speculate for a while on the length and number of caverns and passages contained and then return to his hotel and dream of a large interrogation point framed in the mouth of the dark tunnel. It finally became too much for the doctor, and he attempted to bribe the guides by offering sums which came little short of being fabulous. Not one of them, however, would go with him.

At last, William, the famous colored guide, showed signs of his love of money predominating over his love of life, and the doctor worried the poor darkey until he won his reluctant consent to accompany him. The two provided themselves with the necessary articles and, one day, made their way stealthily along the passages toward the Covered Pit.

The uniqueness of the doctor's scheme is apparent at once. As the authorities had forbidden it, they must steal into the cave without their knowledge and consequently their fate would be unknown. No one would ever know what became of Dr. Hoovey and William. The Covered Pit would withhold its story of the tragedy until the Resurrection Morn.

A few pleasant thoughts like these crowded into the doctor's brain as he made

his way along the cavern. He was half con-
strained to turn back and at least leave a letter telling where he had gone. He was half-
minded to turn back, anyhow. But there was
William trudging stolidly along ahead of him,
and the doctor settled his nerves and pushed
on.

They arrived at the edge of the pit and
stood together trying to pierce the gloom in
the openings between the slabs.

"It will make a right big grave," said
William contemplating the pit.

The doctor started but kept silent.

The two adventurers sat down on a
boulder and made deliberate plans covering
any casualty that might occur. It was also decided, with no indecent haggling whatever,
that William should go first.

The guide tightened everything about
him, and placed his torch in his hat that he
might have both hands free.

Getting down on his hands and knees,
he commenced to make his way like a cat on
very tender ice. It was a moment of supreme
suspense to both. The guide's labored breathing was plainly audible as he slowly moved
along. The doctor shut his eyes at times and
waited with almost a desire, the tension was
so terrible, for the sudden grinding noise;
then the awful roar that would announce to
him that the covering had fallen. But William's light gleamed on the other side and he
was safe. It was now the doctor's turn. William shouted a few directions about the bad
places. Then the doctor started. On his
hands and knees as the guide had been, the
doctor would thrust one hand forward and,

finding a firm place, would bring the other one forward. Some of the slabs slanted frightfully and were damp and slippery. The doctor's life depended on the grip of his fingers.

When about half-way across, the doctor's hand loosened a slab ahead of him which had no connection with the structure of the cover but simply lay on one of the others.

With an awful sound the stone slid off the lower slab and plunged down into the pit. The explorer gave himself up for lost. As the movement of the stone was communicated to the slab on which he crouched, he thought he was gone. A second later when the sounds ceased he could hardly believe that he was still on the cover.

The sensations of the poor guide can only be imagined. Let alone the depressing effects on one's spirits that the horrible death of a companion in the bowels of the earth would have, the guide would be in a sorry plight indeed. With the doctor and the cover at the bottom of the pit, he was alive in his tomb.

His bridge was burned behind him. His only known means of exit was across the covering to the pit and if the cover broke, William was in a bad way. The darkey's teeth chattered as he heard the sound of the falling slab.

But the torch still flickered out over the pit and began to come nearer and nearer. A few more minutes of suspense and the doctor of divinity and the ignorant guide clutched each others' hands in the most affectionate manner possible.

The explorers proceeded along the tun-

nel. They were then on ground trod by no
man before, and the doctor was in his glory.
They spent two days in the new regions and
had some startling adventures but returned
safely across the Covered Pit. When the sunlight beamed on their delighted visions, they
looked at each other for a moment without
speaking. Then the doctor remarked that he
guessed he wouldn't explore any more caves
for awhile and William said he reckoned he
needed a vacation, too.

THE OCTOPUSH

[*No dateline*] Four men once upon a time went into the wilderness seeking for pickerel. They proceeded to a pond which is different from all other sheets of water in the world, excepting the remaining ponds in Sullivan County. A scrawny stone dam, clinging in apparent desperation to its foundation, wandered across a wild valley. In the beginning, the baffled waters had retreated to a forest. In consequence, the four men confronted a sheet of water from which there upreared countless gray, haggard tree-trunks. Squat stumps, in multitudes, stretched long, lazy roots over the surface of the water. Floating logs and sticks bumped gently against the dam. All manner of weeds throttled the lilies and dragged them down. Great pine trees came from all sides to the pond's edge.

In their journey, the four men encountered a creature with a voice from a tomb. His person was concealed behind an enormous straw hat. In graveyard accents, he demanded that he be hired to assist them in their quest. They agreed. From a recess of the bank, he produced a blunt-ended boat, painted a very light blue, with yellow finishings, in accordance with Sullivan aesthetics. Two sculls, whittled from docile pine boards, lay under the seats. Pegs were driven into the boat's side, at convenient rowlock intervals. In deep, impressive tones, the disguised indi-

vidual told the four men that, to his knowledge, the best way to catch pickerel was to
"kidder fur 'em from them there stumps."
The four men clambered into the beautiful
boat and the individual maneuvered his craft
until he had dealt out to four low-spreading
stumps, four fishers. He thereupon repaired
to a fifth stump where he tied his boat. Perch-
ing himself upon the stump-top, he valiantly
grasped a mildewed corncob between his
teeth, ladened with black, eloquent tobacco.
At a distance it smote the senses of the four
men.

The sun gleamed merrily upon the waters, the gaunt, towering tree-trunks and the
stumps lying like spatters of wood which had
dropped from the clouds. Troops of blue and
silver darningneedles danced over the surface.
Bees bustled about the weeds which grew in
the shallow places. Butterflies flickered in the
air. Down in the water, millions of fern
branches quavered and hid mysteries. The
four men sat still and skiddered. The individual puffed tremendously. Ever and anon,
one of the four would cry ecstatically, or
swear madly. His fellows, upon standing to
gaze at him, would either find him holding a
stout fish or nervously struggling with a hook
and line entangled in the hordes of vindictive
weeds and sticks on the bottom. They had
fortune, for the pickerel is a voracious fish.
His only faults are in method. He has a habit
of furiously charging the fleeting bit of glitter
and then darting under a log or around a
corner with it.

At noon, the individual corraled the entire outfit upon a stump, where they lunched

while he entertained them with anecdote.
Afterward, he redistributed them, each to his
personal stump. They fished. He contemplated the scene and made observations which
rang across the water to the four men in bass
solos. Toward the close of the day, he grew
evidently thoughtful, indulging in no more
spasmodic philosophy. The four men fished
intently until the sun had sunk down to some
tree-tops and was peering at them like the
face of an angry man over a hedge. Then one
of the four stood up and shouted across to
where the individual sat enthroned upon the
stump.

"You had better take us ashore, now."
The other three repeated. "Yes, come take
us ashore."

Whereupon the individual carefully
took an erect position. Then, waving a great
yellow-brown bottle and tottering, he gave
vent to a sepulchral roar.

"You fellersh—hic—kin all go—hic—ter
blazersh."

The sun slid down and threw a flare
upon the silence, coloring it red. The man
who had stood up drew a long, deep breath
and sat down heavily. Stupefaction rested
upon the four men.

Dusk came and fought a battle with the
flare before their eyes. Tossing shadows and
red beams mingled in combat. Then the
stillness of evening lay upon the waters.

The individual began to curse in deep
maudlin tones. "Dern fools," he said, "Dern
fools! Why don't'cher g'home?"

"He's full as a fiddler," said the little
man on the third stump. The rest groaned.

They sat facing the stump whereon the individual perched, beating them with mighty oaths. Occasionally he took a drink from the bottle. "Shay, you'm fine lot fellers," he bellowed, "why blazersh don't'cher g'home?"

The little man on the third stump pondered. He got up finally and made oration. He, in the beginning, elaborated the many good qualities which he alleged the individual possessed. Next he painted graphically the pitiful distress and woe of their plight. Then he described the reward due to the individual if he would relieve them, and ended with an earnest appeal to the humanity of the individual, alleging, again, his many virtues. The object of the address struggled to his feet, and in a voice of faraway thunder, said: "Dern fool, g'home." The little man sat down and swore crimson oaths.

A night wind began to roar and clouds bearing a load of rain appeared in the heavens and threatened their position. The four men shivered and turned up their coat collars. Suddenly it struck each that he was alone, separated from humanity by impassable gulfs. All those things which come forth at night began to make noises. Unseen animals scrambled and flopped among the weeds and sticks. Weird features masqueraded awfully in robes of shadow. Each man felt that he was compelled to sit on something that was damply alive. A legion of frogs in the grass by the shore and a host of toads in the trees chanted. The little man started up and shrieked that all creeping things were inside his stump. Then he tried to sit facing four ways, because dread objects were approaching at his back. The individual was drinking and hoarsely singing. At different times they labored with him. It availed them nought. "G'home, dern fools." Among themselves they broached various plans for escape. Each involved a contact with the black water, in which were things that wriggled. They shuddered and sat still.

A ghost-like mist came and hung upon the waters. The pond became a graveyard. The gray tree-trunks and dark logs turned to monuments and crypts. Fireflies were wisp-lights dancing over graves, and then, taking regular shapes, appeared like brass nails in crude caskets. The individual began to gibber. A gibber in a bass voice appals the stoutest heart. It is the declamation of a genie. The little man began to sob; another groaned and the two remaining, being timid by nature, swore great lurid oaths which blazed against the sky.

Suddenly the individual sprang up and gave tongue to a yell which raised the hair on the four men's heads and caused the waters to ruffle. Chattering, he sprang into the boat and grasping an oar paddled frantically to the little man's stump. He tumbled out and cowered at the little man's feet, looking toward his stump with eyes that saw the unknown.

"Stump turned inter an octopush. I was a-settin' on his mouth," he howled.

The little man kicked him.

"Legs all commenced move, dern octopush!" moaned the shrunken individual.

The little man kicked him. But others

cried out against him, so directly he left off. Climbing into the boat he went about collecting his companions. They then proceeded to the stump whereon the individual lay staring wild-eyed at his "octopush." They gathered his limp form into the boat and rowed ashore. "How far is it to the nearest house?" they demanded savagely of him. "Four miles," he replied in a voice of cave-damp. The four men cursed him and built a great fire of pine sticks. They sat by it all night and listened to the individual who dwelt in phantom shadows by the water's edge dismally crooning about an "octopush."

A GHOUL'S ACCOUNTANT

THE STORY OF A SULLIVAN COUNTY
PRODUCE DEAL

[No dateline] In a wilderness sunlight is
noise. Darkness is a great, tremendous silence, accented by small and distant sounds.
The music of the wind in the trees is songs of
loneliness, hymns of abandonment, and lays
of the absence of things congenial and alive.

Once a campfire lay dying in a fit of
temper. A few weak flames struggled choler-
ically among the burned-out logs. Beneath, a
mass of angry, red coals glowered and hated
the world. Some hemlocks sighed and sung,
and a wind purred in the grass. The moon
was looking through the locked branches at
four imperturbable bundles of blankets
which lay near the agonized campfire. The
fire groaned in its last throes, but the bundles
made no sign.

Off in the gloomy unknown a foot fell
upon a twig. The laurel leaves shivered at
the stealthy passing of danger. A moment
later a man crept into the spot of dim light.
His skin was fiercely red and his whiskers infinitely black. He gazed at the four passive
bundles and smiled a smile that curled his
lips and showed yellow, disordered teeth. The
campfire threw up two lurid arms and, quivering, expired. The voices of the trees grew
hoarse and frightened. The bundles were
stolid.

The intruder stepped softly nearer and

looked at the bundles. One was shorter than the others. He regarded it for some time motionless. The hemlocks quavered nervously and the grass shook. The intruder slid to the short bundle and touched it. Then he smiled. The bundle partially upreared itself, and the head of a little man appeared.

"Lord!" he said. He found himself looking at the grin of a ghoul condemned to torment.

"Come," croaked the ghoul.

"What?" said the little man. He began to feel his flesh slide to and fro on his bones as he looked into this smile.

"Come," croaked the ghoul.

"What?" the little man whispered. He grew gray and could not move his legs. The ghoul lifted a three-pronged pickerel-spear and flashed it near the little man's throat. He saw menace on its points. He struggled heavily to his feet.

He cast his eyes upon the remaining mummy-like bundles, but the ghoul confronted his face with the spear.

"Where?" shivered the little man.

The ghoul turned and pointed into the darkness. His countenance shone with lurid light of triumph.

"Go!" he croaked.

The little man blindly staggered in the direction indicated. The three bundles by the fire were still immovable. He tried to pierce the cloth with a glance and opened his mouth to whoop, but the spear ever threatened his face.

The bundles were left far in the rear, and the little man stumbled on alone with the ghoul. Tangled thickets tripped him, saplings buffeted him, and stones turned away from his feet. Blinded and badgered, he began to swear frenziedly. A foam drifted to his mouth, and his eyes glowed with a blue light.

"Go on!" thunderously croaked the ghoul.

The little man's blood turned to salt. His eyes began to decay and refused to do their office. He fell from gloom to gloom.

At last a house was before them. Through a yellow-papered window shone an uncertain light. The ghoul conducted his prisoner to the uneven threshold and kicked the decrepit door. It swung groaning back, and he dragged the little man into a room.

A soiled oil-lamp gave a feeble light that turned the pineboard walls and furniture a dull orange. Before a table sat a wild, gray man. The ghoul threw his victim upon a chair and went and stood by the man. They regarded the little man with eyes that made wheels revolve in his soul.

He cast a dazed glance about the room and saw vaguely that it was dishevelled as from a terrific scuffle. Chairs lay shattered, and dishes in the cupboard were ground to pieces. Destruction had been present. There were moments of silence. The ghoul and the wild, gray man contemplated their victim. A throe of fear passed over him and he sank limp in his chair. His eyes swept feverishly over the faces of his tormentors.

At last the ghoul spoke.

"Well!" he said to the wild, gray man.

The other cleared his throat and stood up.

"Stranger," he said, suddenly, "how much is thirty-three bushels of pertaters at sixty-four an' a half a bushel?"

The ghoul leaned forward to catch the reply. The wild, gray man straightened his figure and listened. A fierce light shone on their faces. Their breaths came swiftly. The little man wriggled his legs in agony.

"Twenty-one, no, two, six and . . ."

"Quick!" hissed the ghoul, hoarsely.

"Twenty-one dollars and twenty-eight cents and a half," laboriously stuttered the little man.

The ghoul gave a tremendous howl.

"There, Tom Jones, dearn yer!" he yelled, "what did I tell yer! hey? Hain't I right? See? Didn't I tell yer that?"

The wild, gray man's body shook. He was delivered of a frightful roar. He sprang forward and kicked the little man out of the door.

THE BLACK DOG

A NIGHT OF SPECTRAL TERROR

[*No dateline*] There was a ceaseless rumble in the air as the heavy rain-drops battered upon the laurel-thickets and the matted moss and haggard rocks beneath. Four water-soaked men made their difficult ways through the drenched forest. The little man stopped and shook an angry finger at where night was stealthily following them. "Cursed be fate and her children and her children's children! We are everlastingly lost!" he cried. The panting procession halted under some dripping, drooping hemlocks and swore in wrathful astonishment.

"It will rain for forty days and forty nights," said the pudgy man, moaningly, "and I feel like a wet loaf of bread now. We shall never find our way out of this wilderness until I am made into a porridge."

In desperation, they started again to drag their listless bodies through the watery bushes. After a time, the clouds withdrew from above them, and great winds came from concealment and went sweeping and swirling among the trees. Night also came very near and menaced the wanderers with darkness. The little man had determination in his legs. He scrambled among the thickets and made desperate attempts to find a path or road. As he climbed a hillock, he espied a small clearing upon which sat desolation and a venerable house, wept over by wind-waved pines.

"Ho," he cried, "here's a house."

His companions straggled painfully after him as he fought the thickets between him and the cabin. At their approach, the wind frenziedly opposed them and skirled madly in the trees. The little man boldly confronted the weird glances from the crannies of the cabin and rapped on the door. A score of timbers answered with groans and, within, something fell to the floor with a clang.

"Ho," said the little man. He stepped back a few paces.

Somebody in a distant part started and walked across the floor toward the door with an ominous step. A slate-colored man appeared. He was dressed in a ragged shirt and trousers, the latter stuffed into his boots. Large tears were falling from his eyes.

"How-d'-do, my friend?" said the little man, affably.

"My ol' uncle, Jim Crocker, he's sick ter death," replied the slate-colored person.

"Ho," said the little man. "Is that so?"

The latter's clothing clung desperately to him and water sogged in his boots. He stood patiently on one foot for a time.

"Can you put us up here until to-morrow?" he asked, finally.

"Yes," said the slate-colored man.

The party passed into a little unwashed room, inhabited by a stove, a stairway, a few precarious chairs and a misshapen table.

"I'll fry yer some po'k and make yer some coffee," said the slate-colored man to his guests.

"Go ahead, old boy," cried the little man cheerfully from where he sat on the table, smoking his pipe and dangling his legs.

"My ol' uncle, Jim Crocker, he's sick ter death," said the slate-colored man.

"Think he'll die?" asked the pudgy man, gently.

"No!"

"No?"

"He won't die! He's an ol' man, but he won't die, yit! The black dorg hain't been around yit!"

"The black dog?" said the little man, feebly. He struggled with himself for a moment.

"What's the black dog?" he asked at last.

"He's a sperrit," said the slate-colored man in a voice of sombre hue.

"Oh, he is? Well?"

"He hants these parts, he does, an' when people are goin' to die, he comes and sets and howls."

"Ho," said the little man. He looked out of the window and saw night making a million shadows.

The little man moved his legs nervously.

"I don't believe in these things," said he, addressing the slate-colored man, who was scuffling with a side of pork.

"Wot things?" came incoherently from the combatant.

"Oh, these—er—phantoms and ghosts and what not. All rot, I say."

"That's because you have merely a stomach and no soul," grunted the pudgy man.

"Ho, old pudgkins!" replied the little man. His back curved with passion. A tempest of wrath was in the pudgy man's eye. The final epithet used by the little man was a carefully-studied insult, always brought forth at a crisis. They quarrelled.

"All right, pudgkins, bring on your phantom," cried the little man in conclusion.

His stout companion's wrath was too huge for words. The little man smiled triumphantly. He had staked his opponent's reputation.

The visitors sat silent. The slate-colored man moved about in a small personal atmosphere of gloom.

Suddenly, a strange cry came to their ears from somewhere. It was a low, trembling call which made the little man quake privately in his shoes. The slate-colored man bounded at the stairway and disappeared with a flash of legs through a hole in the ceiling. The party below heard two voices in conversation, one belonging to the slate-colored man and the other in the quivering tones of age. Directly the slate-colored man reappeared from above and said: "The ol' man is took bad for his supper."

He hurriedly prepared a mixture with hot water, salt and beef. Beef-tea, it might be called. He disappeared again. Once more the party below heard, vaguely, talking over their heads. The voice of age arose to a shriek.

"Open the window, fool! Do you think I can live in the smell of your soup?"

Mutterings by the slate-colored man and the creaking of a window were heard.

The slate-colored man stumbled down

the stairs and said with intense gloom. "The black dorg'll be along soon."

The little man started, and the pudgy man sneered at him. They ate a supper and then sat waiting. The pudgy man listened so palpably that the little man wished to kill him. The wood-fire became excited and sputtered frantically. Without, a thousand spirits of the winds had become entangled in the pine branches and were lowly pleading to be loosened. The slate-colored man tiptoed across the room and lit a timid candle. The men sat waiting.

The phantom dog lay cuddled to a round bundle, asleep down the roadway against the windward side of an old shanty. The spectre's master had moved to Pike County. But the dog lingered as a friend might linger at the tomb of a friend. His fur was like a suit of old clothes. His jowls hung and flopped, exposing his teeth. Yellow famine was in his eyes. The wind-rocked shanty groaned and muttered, but the dog slept. Suddenly, however, he got up and shambled to the roadway. He cast a long glance from his hungry, despairing eyes in the direction of the venerable house. The breeze came full to his nostrils. He threw back his head and gave a long, low howl and started intently up the road. Maybe he smelled a dead man.

The group around the fire in the venerable house were listening and waiting. The atmosphere of the room was tense. The slate-colored man's face was twitching and his drabbed hands were gripped together. The little man was continually looking behind his chair. Upon the countenance of the pudgy man appeared conceit for an approaching triumph over the little man, mingled with apprehension for his own safety. Five pipes glowed as rivals of the timid candle. Profound silence drooped heavily over them. Finally the slate-colored man spoke.

"My ol' uncle, Jim Crocker, he's sick ter death."

The four men started and then shrank back in their chairs.

"Damn it!" replied the little man, vaguely.

Again there was a long silence. Suddenly it was broken by a wild cry from the room above. It was a shriek that struck upon them with appalling swiftness, like a flash of lightning. The walls whirled and the floor rumbled. It brought the men together with a rush. They huddled in a heap and stared at white terror in each other's faces. The slate-colored man grasped the candle and flared it above his head. "The black dorg," he howled, and plunged at the stairway. The maddened four men followed frantically, for it is better to be in the presence of the awful than only within hearing.

Their ears still quivering with the shriek, they bounded through the hole in the ceiling and into the sickroom.

With quilts drawn closely to his shrunken breast for a shield, his bony hand gripping the cover, an old man lay, with glazing eyes fixed on the open window. His throat gurgled and a froth appeared at his mouth.

From the outer darkness came a strange, unnatural wail, burdened with weight of death and each note filled with foreboding. It was the song of the spectral dog.

"God!" screamed the little man. He ran to the open window. He could see nothing at first save the pine-trees engaged in a furious combat, tossing back and forth and struggling. The moon was peeping cautiously over the rims of some black clouds. But the chant of the phantom guided the little man's eyes, and he at length perceived its shadowy form on the ground under the window. He fell away gasping at the sight. The pudgy man crouched in a corner, chattering insanely. The slate-colored man, in his fear, crooked his legs and looked like a hideous Chinese idol. The man upon the bed was turned to stone, save the froth, which pulsated.

In the final struggle, terror will fight the inevitable. The little man roared maniacal curses and, rushing again to the window, began to throw various articles at the spectre.

A mug, a plate, a knife, a fork, all crashed or clanged on the ground, but the song of the spectre continued. The bowl of beef-tea followed. As it struck the ground the phantom ceased its cry.

The men in the chamber sank limply against the walls, with the unearthly wail still ringing in their ears and the fear unfaded from their eyes. They waited again.

The little man felt his nerves vibrate. Destruction was better than another wait. He grasped a candle and, going to the window, held it over his head and looked out.

"Ho!" he said.

His companions crawled to the window and peered out with him.

"He's eatin' the beef-tea," said the slate-colored man, faintly.

"The damn dog was hungry," said the pudgy man.

"There's your phantom," said the little man to the pudgy man.

On the bed, the old man lay dead. Without, the spectre was wagging its tail.

A TENT IN AGONY

A SULLIVAN COUNTY SKETCH

FOUR MEN once came to a wet place in the roadless forest to fish. They pitched their tent fair upon the brow of a pine-clothed ridge of riven rocks whence a bowlder could be made to crash through the brush and whirl past the trees to the lake below. On fragrant hemlock boughs they slept the sleep of unsuccessful fishermen, for upon the lake alternately the sun made them lazy and the rain made them wet. Finally they ate the last bit of bacon and smoked and burned the last fearful and wonderful hoecake.

Immediately a little man volunteered to stay and hold the camp while the remaining three should go the Sullivan County miles to a farmhouse for supplies. They gazed at him dismally. "There's only one of you—the devil make a twin," they said in parting malediction, and disappeared down the hill in the known direction of a distant cabin. When it came night and the hemlocks began to sob they had not returned. The little man sat close to his companion, the campfire, and encouraged it with logs. He puffed fiercely at a heavy built brier, and regarded a thousand shadows which were about to assault him. Suddenly he heard the approach of the unknown, crackling the twigs and rustling the dead leaves. The little man arose slowly to his feet, his clothes refused to fit his back, his pipe dropped from his mouth, his knees smote each other. "Hah!" he bellowed hoarsely in menace. A growl replied and a bear paced into the light of the fire. The little man supported himself upon a sapling and regarded his visitor.

The bear was evidently a veteran and a fighter, for the black of his coat had become tawny with age. There was confidence in his gait and arrogance in his small, twinkling eyes. He rolled back his lips and disclosed his white teeth. The fire magnified the red of his mouth. The little man had never before confronted the terrible and he could not wrest it from his breast. "Hah!" he roared. The bear interpreted this as the challenge of a gladiator. He approached warily. As he came near, the boots of fear were suddenly upon the little man's feet. He cried out and then darted around the campfire. "Ho!" said the bear to himself, "this thing won't fight—it runs. Well, suppose I catch it." So upon his features there fixed the animal look of going—somewhere. He started intensely around the campfire. The little man shrieked and ran furiously. Twice around they went.

The hand of heaven sometimes falls heavily upon the righteous. The bear gained.

In desperation the little man flew into the tent. The bear stopped and sniffed at the entrance. He scented the scent of many men. Finally he ventured in.

The little man crouched in a distant corner. The bear advanced, creeping, his blood burning, his hair erect, his jowls dripping. The little man yelled and rustled clumsily under the flap at the end of the tent. The

bear snarled awfully and made a jump and a
grab at his disappearing game. The little
man, now without the tent, felt a tremendous
paw grab his coat tails. He squirmed and
wriggled out of his coat, like a schoolboy in
the hands of an avenger. The bear howled
triumphantly and jerked the coat into the
tent and took two bites, a punch and a hug
before he discovered his man was not in it.
Then he grew not very angry, for a bear on a
spree is not a black-haired pirate. He is
merely a hoodlum. He lay down on his back,
took the coat on his four paws and began to
play uproariously with it. The most appalling,
blood-curdling whoops and yells came to
where the little man was crying in a treetop
and froze his blood. He moaned a little
speech meant for a prayer and clung convulsively to the bending branches. He gazed
with tearful wistfulness at where his comrade,
the campfire, was giving dying flickers and
crackles. Finally, there was a roar from the
tent which eclipsed all roars; a snarl which it
seemed would shake the stolid silence of the
mountain and cause it to shrug its granite
shoulders. The little man quaked and shrivelled to a grip and a pair of eyes. In the glow
of the embers he saw the white tent quiver
and fall with a crash. The bear's merry play
had disturbed the centre pole and brought a
chaos of canvas about his head.

Now the little man became the witness of
a mighty scene. The tent began to flounder.
It took flopping strides in the direction of the
lake. Marvelous sounds came from within—
rips and tears, and great groans and pants.
The little man went into giggling hysterics.

STEPHEN CRANE: SULLIVAN COUNTY TALES AND SKETCHES 108

The entangled monster failed to extricate himself before he had frenziedly walloped the tent to the edge of the mountain. So it came to pass that three men, clambering up the hill with bundles and baskets, saw their tent approaching.

It seemed to them like a white-robed phantom pursued by hornets. Its moans riffled the hemlock twigs.

The three men dropped their bundles and scurried to one side, their eyes gleaming with fear. The canvas avalanche swept past them. They leaned, faint and dumb, against trees and listened, their blood stagnant. Below them it struck the base of a great pine tree, where it writhed and struggled. The three watched its convolutions a moment and then started terrifically for the top of the hill. As they disappeared, the bear cut loose with a mighty effort. He cast one dishevelled and agonized look at the white thing, and then started wildly for the inner recesses of the forest.

The three fear-stricken individuals ran to the rebuilt fire. The little man reposed by it calmly smoking. They sprang at him and overwhelmed him with interrogations. He contemplated darkness and took a long, pompous puff. "There's only one of me—and the devil made a twin," he said.

AN EXPLOSION
OF SEVEN BABIES

A SULLIVAN COUNTY SKETCH

A LITTLE MAN was sweating and swearing his way through an intricate forest. His hat was pushed indignantly to the far rear of his head, and upon his perspiring features there was a look of conscious injury.

Suddenly he perceived ahead of him a high stone wall against which waves of bushes surged. The little man fought his way to the wall and looked over it.

A brown giantess was working in a potato patch. Upon a bench, under the eaves of a worn-out house, seven babies were wailing and rubbing their stomachs.

"Ho!" said the little man to himself.

He stood, observant, for a few moments. Then he climbed painfully over the wall and came to a stand in the potato patch. His eyes wandered to the seven babies wailing and rubbing their stomachs. Their mournful music fascinated him.

"Madam," he said, as he took off his hat and bowed, "I have unfortunately lost my way. Could you direct—" He suddenly concluded: "Great Scott!"

He had turned his eyes from the seven babies to the brown giantess and saw upon

---

Title is as given in the holograph MS in the Barrett Crane Collection, from which our text is drawn, correcting the text in the *Home Magazine,* Vol. 16 (January 1901), with its altered title: "A Sullivan County Episode."

her face the glare of a tigress. Her fingers
were playing convulsively over her hoe-handle
and the muscles of her throat were swollen
and wriggling. Her eyes were glowing with
fury. She came forward with the creeping
motion of an animal about to spring.

The little man gave a backward leap.
Tremendous astonishment enwrapped him
and trepidation showed in his legs.

"G-good heavens, madam," he stuttered.
He threw up one knee and held his spread
fingers before his face. His mouth was puck-
ered to an amazed whistle.

The giantess stood before him, her hands
upon her hips, her lips curled in a snarl. She
followed closely as the little man retreated
backward step by step toward the fence, his
eyes staring in bewilderment.

"For the love of Mike, madam, what ails
you?" he spluttered.

He saw here an avenger. Wherefore he
knew not, but he momentarily expected to be
smitten to a pulp.

"Beast!" roared the giantess, suddenly.
She reached forth and grasped the arm of the
palsied little man who cast a despairing glance
at the high, stone wall. She twisted him about
and then, raising a massive arm, pointed to
the row of seven babies, who, as if they had
gotten a cue, burst out like a brass band.

"Well, what the devil—" roared the little
man.

"Beast!" howled the giantess, "It made'm
sick! They ate ut! That dum fly-paper!" The
babies began to frantically beat their stomachs
with their fists.

"Villain!" shrieked the giantess. The little man felt the winding fingers crush the flesh and bone of his arm. The giantess began to roar like a dragon. She bended over and braced herself. Then her iron arms forced the little man to his knees.

He knew he was going to be eaten. He moaned hoarsely.

He arrived at the critical stage of degradation. He would resist. He touched some hidden spring in his being and went off like a fire-work. The man became a tumult. Every muscle in his body he made perform a wriggling contortion. The giantess plunged forward and kneaded him as if he were bread unbaked.

From over the stone wall came the swishing sound of moving bushes, unheard by the combatants. Presently the face of a pudgy man, tranquil in its wrinkles, appeared. Amazement instantly smote him in his tracks and he hung heavily to the stones.

From the potato patch arose a cloud of dust, pregnant with curses. In it he could dimly see the little man in a state of revolution. His legs flashed in the air like a pinwheel. The pudgy man stared with gleaming eyes at the kaleidoscope. He climbed upon the wall to get a better view. Some bellowing animal seemed to have his friend in its claws.

It soon became evident to the little man that he could not eternally revolve and kick in such a manner. He felt his blood begin to dry up and his muscles turn to paste. Those frightful talons were squeezing his life away. His mangled arms were turning weak. He was about to be subdued.

But here the pudgy man, in his excitement, performed the feat of his life. He fell off the wall, giving an involuntary shout, and landed, with a flop, in the potato patch.

The brown giantess snarled. She hurled the little man from her and turned, with a toss of her dishevelled locks, to face a new foe. The pudgy man quaked miserably and yelled an unintelligible explanation or apology or prayer. The brow of the giantess was black and she strided with ferocious menace toward him.

The little man had fallen in a chaotic mass among the potato hills. He struggled to his feet. Somehow, his blood was hot in his veins and he started to bristle courageously in reinforcement of his friend. But suddenly he changed his mind and made off at high speed, leaving the pudgy man to his fate.

His unchosen course lay directly toward the seven babies who, in their anxiety to view the combat, had risen from the bench and were standing, ready as a Roman populace, to signify the little man's death by rubbing their stomachs. Intent upon the struggle, they had forgotten to howl.

But when they perceived the headlong charge of the little man, they, as a unit, exploded. It was like the sudden clang of an alarm bell to the brown giantess. She wheeled from the pudgy man, who climbed the wall, fell off, in his haste, into the bushes on the other side and, later, allowed but half of his head to appear over the top of it.

The giantess perceived the little man about to assault her seven babies, whose mouths were in a state of eruption. She howled, grabbed a hoe from the ground, and pursued.

The little man shied from the protesting babies and ran like a grey-hound. He flung himself over a high fence. Then he waited. Curiosity held him. He had been mopped and dragged, punched and pounded, bitten and scratched. He wished to know why.

The brown giantess, mad with rage, crashed against the fence. She shook her huge fist at the little man.

"Drat yeh!" she roared.

She began to climb the fence. It is not well to behold a woman climb a fence. The little man yelled and ran off.

He stumbled and tore through a brush lot and bounced terrifically into the woods. As he halted to get breath, he heard above the sound of the wind laughing in the trees a final explosion by the seven babies as, perhaps, they perceived the brown giantess returning empty handed to the worn-out house.

As the little man went on into the woods, he perceived a crouching figure with terror-gleaming eyes. He whistled and drew near it. Directly, the little man, bedraggled, dirt-stained, bloody and amazed, confronted the pudgy man, perspiring, limp, dusty and astonished. They gazed at each other profoundly.

Finally, the little man broke the silence.

"Devilish mysterious business," he said, slowly. The pudgy man had a thousand questions in his eyes.

"What in Heaven's name, Billie—" he blurted.

The little man waved his hand. "Don't ask me. I don't know anything about it."

"What?"

"No more'n a rabbit. She said something

about fly-paper and the kids, that's all I know."

The pudgy man drew a long breath. "Great Lord," he said. They sat down on a log and thought.

At last, the little man got up and yawned. "I can't make head nor tail of the bloomin' business," he said wearily. They walked slowly off through the day-gloom of the woods. "I wish she hadn't called me a beast. I didn't like that," added the little man, musingly, after a time.

In a shady spot on a highway, they found their two companions who were lazily listening to a short stranger who was holding forth at some length and with apparent enthusiasm. At the approach of the little man and the pudgy man, the short man turned to them with a smile.

"Gentlemen," he said, "I have here a wonder of the age, which I wish to present to your intelligent notice. Smither's Eternal Fly Annihilating Paper is—"

The little man frothed at the mouth and cursed. Before his comrades could intervene he sprang forward and kicked the short man heavily in the stomach.

THE CRY OF A
HUCKLEBERRY PUDDING

A DIM STUDY OF
CAMPING EXPERIENCES

A GREAT BLAZE wavered redly against the blackness of the night in the pines. Before the eyes of his expectant companions, a little man moved with stately dignity as the creator of a huckleberry pudding.

"I know how to make'm," he said in a confident voice, "just exactly right."

The others looked at him with admiration and they sat down to eat.

After a time, a pudgy man whose spoon was silent, said: "I don't like this much."

"What?" cried the little man, threateningly.

"I don't seem to get on with it," said the pudgy man. He looked about for support in the faces of his companions. "I don't like it, somehow," he added slowly.

"Fool!" roared the little man, furiously. "You're mad because you didn't make it. I never saw such a beast."

The pudgy man wrapped himself in a great dignity. He glanced suggestingly at the plates of the two others. They were intact.

"Ho," cried the little man, "you're all idiots."

He saw that he must vindicate his work.

Reprinted from *University Herald* (Syracuse): December 23, 1892. Reprinted in *Chap Book* (Syracuse University literary magazine): May 1930.

He must eat it. He sat before them and, with ineffable bliss lighting his countenance, ate all of the huckleberry pudding. Then he laid aside his plate, lighted his pipe and addressed his companions as unappreciative block-heads.

The pipe, the fire and the song of the pines soothed him after a time and he puffed tranquilly. The four men sat staring vacantly at the blaze until the spirits of the tent at the edge of the fire circle in drowsy voices began to call them. Their thoughts became heavily fixed on the knee-deep bed of hemlock. One by one they arose, knocked ashes from their pipes and, treading softly to the open flaps, disappeared. Alone, the camp-fire spluttered valiantly for a time, opposing its music to the dismal crooning of the trees that accented the absence of things congenial and alive. A curious moon peered through locked branches at imperturbable bundles of blankets which lay in the shadows of the tent.

The fragrant blackness of the early night passed away and grey ghost-mists came winding slowly up from the marshes and stole among the wet tree trunks. Wavering leaves dotted with dewdrops glowed in a half-light of impending dawn. From the tent came sounds of heavy sleeping. The bundles of blankets clustered on the hemlock twigs.

Suddenly from off in the thickets of gloom, there came a cry. It seemed to crash on the tent. It smote the bundles of blankets. There was instant profound agitation, a whirling chaos of coverings, legs and arms; then, heads appeared. The men had heard the voice of the unknown crying in the wilderness, and it made their souls quaver.

They had slumbered through the trees'
song of loneliness and the lay of isolation of
the mountain-grass. Hidden frogs had muttered ominously since night-fall, and distant
owls, undoubtedly perched on lofty branches
and silhouetted by the moon, had hooted.
There had been an endless hymning by
leaves, blades, and unseen live things, through
which these men, who adored Wagner, had
slept.

But a false note in the sounds of night
had convulsed them. A strange tune had made
them writhe.

The cry of the unknown instantly awoke
them to terror. It is mightier than the war-
yell of the dreadful, because the dreadful may
be definite. But this whoop strikes greater
fear from hearts because it tells of formidable
mouths and great, grasping claws that live in
impossibility. It is the chant of a phantom
force which imagination declares invincible,
and awful to the sight.

In the tent, eyes a-glitter with terror
gazed into eyes. Knees softly smote each
other and lips trembled.

The pudgy man gave vent to a tremendous question. "What was that?" he whispered.

The others made answer with their
blanched faces. The group, waiting in the
silence that followed their awakening, wriggled their legs in the agony of fright. There
was a pause which extended through space.
Comets hung and worlds waited. Their
thoughts shot back to that moment when
they had started upon the trip, and they were

filled with regret that it had been.

"Oh, goodness, what was that?" repeated the pudgy man, intensely.

Suddenly, their faces twitched and their fingers turned to wax. The cry was repeated. Its burden caused the men to huddle together like drowning kittens. They watched the banshees of the fog drifting lazily among the trees. They saw eyes in the grey obscurity. They heard a thousand approaching footfalls in the rustling of the dead leaves. They grovelled.

Then, they heard the unknown stride to and fro in the forest, giving calls, weighted with challenge, that could makes cities hearing, fear. Roars went to the ends of earth, and snarls that would appall armies turned the men in the tent to a moaning mass with forty eyes. The challenges changed to wailings as of a fever-torn soul. Later, there came snorts of anger that sounded cruel, like the noise of a rampant bull on a babies' play ground. Later still, howls, as from an abandoned being strangling in the waters of trouble.

"Great Scott," roared the pudgy man, "I can't stand this."

He wriggled to his feet and tottered out to the dying fire. His companions followed. They had reached the cellar of fear. They were now resolved to use weapons on the great destruction. They would combat the inevitable. They peered among the trees wherefrom an hundred assaulting shadows came. The unknown was shrieking.

Of a sudden, the pudgy man screamed like a wounded animal.

"It's got Billie," he howled. They discovered that the little man was gone.

To listen or to wait is the most tense of occupations. In their absorption they had not seen that a comrade was missing.

Instantly, their imaginations perceived his form in the clutch of a raging beast.

"Come on," shouted the pudgy man. They grasped bludgeons and rushed valiantly into the darkness. They stumbled from gloom to gloom in a mad rush for their friend's life. The key-note of terror kept clanging in their ears and guided their scrambling feet. Tangled thickets tripped them. Saplings buffeted heroically, and stones turned away. Branches smote their heads so that it appeared as if lightning had flapped its red wings in their faces.

Once, the pudgy man stopped. The unknown was just ahead.

The dim lights of early dawn came charging through the forest. The grey and black of mist and shadow retreated before crimson beams that had advanced to the tree-tops.

The men came to a stand, waving their heads to glance down the aisles of the wilderness.

"There he is," shouted the pudgy man. The party rushing forward came upon the form of the little man, quivering at the foot of a tree. His blood seemed to be turned to salt. From out his wan, white face his eyes shone with a blue light. "Oh, thunderation," he moaned. "Oh, thunderation."

"What?" cried his friends. Their voices shook with anxiety.

"Oh, thunderation," repeated he.

"For the love of Mike tell us, Billie," cried the pudgy man, "What is the matter?"

"Oh, thunderation," wailed the little man. Suddenly he rolled about on the ground and gave vent to a howl that rolled and pealed over the width of forest. Its tones told of death and fear and unpaid debts. It clamored like a song of forgotten war, and died away to the scream of a maiden. The pleadings of fire-surrounded children mingled with the calls of wave-threatened sailors. Two barbaric tribes clashed together on a sun-burnt plain; a score of bare-kneed clansmen crossed claymores amid grey rocks; a woman saw a lover fall; a dog was stabbed in an alley; a steel knight bit dust with bloody mouth; a savage saw a burning home.

The rescuing party leaned weakly against trees. After the little man had concluded, there was a silence.

Finally, the pudgy man advanced. He struggled with his astonished tongue for a moment. "Do you mean to say, Billie," he said at last, "that all that tangled chaos emanated from you?"

The little man made no reply but heaved about on the ground, moaning: "Oh, thunderation."

The three men contemplating him suddenly felt themselves swell with wrath. They had been terrorized to no purpose. They had expected to be eaten. They were not. The fact maddened them. The pudgy man voiced the assembly.

"You infernal little jay, get up off'n the ground and come on," he cried. "You make me sick."

"Oh, thunderation," replied the little man.

The three men began to berate him. They turned into a babble of wrath.

"You scared us to death."

"What do you wanta holler that way for?"

"You're a bloomin' nuisance. For heaven's sake, what are you yellin' about?"

The little man staggered to his feet. Anger took hold of him. He waved his arms eloquently.

"That pudding, you fools," he cried.

His companions paused and regarded him.

"Well," said the pudgy man, eventually, "what in blazes did you eat it for then?"

"Well, I didn't know," roared the other, I didn't know that it was that way."

"You shouldn't have eaten it, anyhow. There was the sin. You shouldn't have eaten it anyway."

"But I didn't know," shouted the little man.

"You should have known," they stormed. You've made idiots of us. You scared us to death with your hollerin'."

As he reeled toward the camp, they followed him, railing like fish-wives.

The little man turned at bay.

"Exaggerated fools," he yelled. "Fools, to apply no salve but moral teaching to a man with the stomach-ache."

THE HOLLER TREE

S THEY went along a narrow wood-path, the little man accidentally stumbled against the pudgy man. The latter was carrying a basket of eggs and he became angry.

"Look out, can't you! Do you wanta break all these eggs? Walk straight—what's the matter with you?" he said and passed on.

The little man saved his balance with difficulty. He had to keep from spilling a pail of milk. "T'blazes with your old eggs," he called out.

The pudgy man spoke over his shoulder. "Well, you needn't have any when we get to camp, then," he said.

"Who wants any of your infernal old eggs. Keep your infernal old eggs," replied the little man.

The four men trudged on into the forest until presently the little man espied a dead tree. He paused. "Look at that tree," he said.

They scrutinized it. It was a tall, gaunt relic of a pine that stood like a yellow warrior still opposing an aged form to blows in storm-battles.

Text is that of the holograph MS (nine sheets) in the Barrett Crane Collection. On verso is the opening of "The Reluctant Voyagers," which was written in May–June of 1893, and also on verso of "The Holler Tree" MS is the beginning of *George's Mother*, a sketch of Mrs. Kelcey which finally appears in Chapter II. "The Holler Tree" was probably written in 1892, but *George's Mother* was likely begun at the same time as "The Reluctant Voyagers," in 1893. "The Holler Tree" was not published until 1934 (in *Golden Book);* Crane probably lost the manuscript by using its backs for the other projects.

"I bet it's got lots of nests in it and all sorts of things like that," murmured the little man. The pudgy man scoffed. "Oh, fudge," he said.

"Well, I bet it has," asserted the other.

The four men put down their loads of provisions and stood around and argued.

"Yes, I bet it's a corner-stone with an almanac in it and a census report and a certified list of the pew-holders," said the pudgy man to the little man.

The latter swore for some time. "Put up even money," he demanded in conclusion. "Put up even money."

"Look out—you'll kick over the eggs," replied the pudgy man.

"Well, put up even money. You daren't."

The pudgy man scornfully kicked a stone. "Oh, fudge. How you going to prove it? Tell me that."

The little man thought. "Well," he said, eventually, "I'll climb up. That's how."

The pudgy man looked at the tree and at the little man. He thought.

"I'll go it," he suddenly decided.

The little man laid down his pipe, tightened his belt and went off and looked at the tree.

"Well—" he began, coming back.

"Go on and climb it," said the pudgy man. "You said you'd climb it."

The little man went off and looked at the tree again. "Well, I will," he said, finally. The pudgy man giggled. The little man tightened his belt more. He approached and put both arms around the tree.

"Say," he said, turning round. "You—I—"

"Go on and climb it," interrupted the

pudgy man. "You said you'd climb it."

The little man began to climb school-boy fashion. He found many difficulties. The wood crumbled and rubbed into his clothes. He felt smeared. Besides there was a horrible strain upon his legs.

When about half way, he ceased wriggling and turned his head cautiously. "Say—"

The three men had been regarding him intently. They then burst out. "Go on! Go on! You've got that far—what's the use of stopping? I believe you're gettin' scared! Oh, my!"

He swore and continued up. Several times he seemed about to fall in a lump. The three below held their breath.

Once, he paused to deliver an oration and forgot his grip for a moment. It was near being fatal.

At last, he reached the top. "Well?" said the pudgy man. The little man gazed about him. There was a sombre sea of pines, rippling in a wind. Far away, there was a little house and two yellow fields.

"Fine scenery up here," he murmured.

"Oh, bother," said the pudgy man. "Where's your nests and all that? That's what I wanta know."

The little man peered down the hollow trunk. "They're in there."

The pudgy man grinned. "How do you know?"

The little man looked down the hole again. "It's all dark," he said.

The pudgy man complacently lit a fresh pipe. "Certainly, it is," he remarked. "You look great up there, don't you? What you goin' to do now, eh?"

The little man balanced himself carefully on the ragged edge and looked thoughtfully at the hole. "Well, I might slide down," he said in a doubtful voice.

"That's it," cried the other. "That's what you wanta do! Slide down!"

"Well," said the little man, "it looks pretty dangerous."

"Oh, I see! You're afraid!"

"I ain't!"

"Yes, you are, too! Else why don't you slide down?"

"Well, how th' devil do I know but what something's down there?" shouted the little man in a rage.

His companion replied with scorn. "Pooh! Nothin' but a hollow tree! You're afraid of the dark!"

"You must take me for a fool! What th' blazes do I wanta be slidin' down every hollow tree I see for?"

"Well, you climbed up, didn't you? What are you up there for? You can't find your little nests and things just settin' there an' cursin', can you? You're afraid, I bet!"

"You make—"

"Oh, yes, you are. You know you are."

The little man flung his legs over and slid down until only his head and his gripping fingers appeared. He seemed to be feeling about with his feet.

"There's nothing to climb down with," he said, finally.

"Certainly not. Did you hope for a stairway? You're afraid."

The little man's face flushed and his eyes grew like beads. He glared from out of the hole.

"I am not, you big—"

"Oh, yes, you are. Anyone can see it."

"Thunderation, you're th'—"

"Oh, come, Billie, either climb down th' outside or slide down th' inside. There's no use of you sittin' up there, you know, if you ain't going to do something. You're afraid, that's what."

"I tell you I ain't. What th' devil—"

"Oh, yes, you are, too. You're pale with fright, Billie. We can see it down here. Oh, my! I'm surprised."

The little man raised a fist. "Thunder and blazes—"

He vanished down the hole.

The wood had crumbled and broken under the strain of the one hand. Hollow sounds of scratchings and thumpings came to the ears of his three companions. In agitation, they ran about the vibrating trunk and called to their comrade in many voices. They were fearful he had met his time.

Presently, they heard a muffled noise of swearing. They listened. Down near the ground, the little man was cursing under forced draft. The old tree shook like a smokestack.

The pudgy man approached and put near his ear.

"Billie!"

"What?"

"Are you inside the tree?"

The little man began to kick and clamor. His voice came in a dull roar. "Certainly I'm inside the tree. Where th' devil did you suppose I was? What th'—"

His voice died away in smothered thunder.

"Well, but, Billie," asked the pudgy man anxiously, "how you going to get out?"

The little man began to rage again. "What a fool you are. I don't know how I'm going to get out. Don't suppose I've got plans made already, do you?"

"Well, I guess you'll have to climb," mused the pudgy man. "That's the only way, and you can't stay in there forever, you know."

The little man made some efforts. There was a sound of rending clothes. Presently he ceased.

"It's no go," he announced.

The three men sat down and debated upon theories.

Finally the little man began to roar at them and kick his prison wall. "Think I wanta stay in here while you fellows hold arguments for a couple of hours? Why th' thunder don't you do something instead of talking so much? What do you think I am anyway?"

The pudgy man approached the tree. "You might as well keep quiet," he said in a grim voice. "You're in there and you might as well keep quiet—"

The little man began to swear.

"Stop your howling," angrily cried the pudgy man. "There's no use of howlin'."

"I won't! It's your fault I'm in here. If it hadn't been for you, I wouldn't'a climbed up."

"Well, I didn't make you fall down inside, anyway. You did that yourself."

"I didn't either. You made me tumble, old pudgkins. If you had minded your own business it would have been all right. It's your stupidity that's got me in here."

"It was your own, you little fool. I—"

The little man began to rave and wriggle. The pudgy man went very near to the tree and stormed. They had a furious quarrel. The eloquence of the little man caused some tremors in the tree, and presently it began to sway gently.

Suddenly, the pudgy man screamed. "You're pushin' th' tree over on me." He started away. The trunk trembled, and tottered, and began to fall. It seemed like a mighty blow aimed by the wrathful little man at the head of the fleeing pudgy man.

The latter bounded, light as a puff-ball, over the ground. His face was white with terror. He turned an agonized somersault into a thicket, as the tree, with a splintering cry, crashed near his heels. He lay in a bush and trembled.

The little man's legs were wagging plaintively from the other end of the trunk. The two remaining men rushed forward with cries of alarm and began to tug at them. The little man came forth, finally. He was of deep bronze hue from a coating of wet dead wood. A soft bed of it came with him. They helped him to his feet. He felt his shoulders and legs with an air of anxiety. After a time, he rubbed the crumbles from his eyes and began to stagger and swear softly.

Suddenly, he perceived the pudgy man lying pale in the bush. He limped over to him.

The pudgy man was moaning. "Lord, it just missed me by 'bout an inch."

The little man thoughtfully contemplated his companion. Presently, a smile was born at the corners of his mouth and grew until it wreathed his face. The pudgy man cursed in an unhappy vein as he was confronted by the little man's grins.

The latter seemed about to deliver an oration but, instead, he turned and, picking up his pail of milk, started away. He paused once and looked back. He pointed with his fore-finger.

"There's your eggs—under the tree," he said.

He resumed his march down the forest pathway. His stride was that of a proud grenadier.

THE SNAKE

WHERE the path wended across the ridge, the bushes of huckleberry and sweet fern swarmed at it in two curling waves until it was a mere winding line traced through a tangle. There was no interference by clouds, and as the rays of the sun fell upon the ridge, they called into voice innumerable insects which chanted the heat of the summer day in steady throbbing unending chorus.

A man and a dog came from the laurel

Text is that of the holograph MS in the Barrett Crane Collection. First published in *Pocket Magazine:* August 1896. Reprinted in *Last Words* (London, 1902).

thickets of the valley where the white brook brawled with the rocks. They followed the deep line of the path across the ridge. The dog—a large lemon and white setter—walked, tranquilly meditative, at his master's heels.

Suddenly from some unknown and yet near place in advance there came a dry shrill whistling rattle that smote motion instantly from the limbs of the man and the dog. Like the fingers of a sudden death, this sound seemed to touch the man at the nape of the neck, at the top of the spine, and change him, as swift as thought, to a statue of listening horror, surprise, rage. The dog, too—the same icy hand was laid upon him and he stood crouched and quivering, his jaw drooping, the froth of terror upon his lips, the light of hatred in his eyes.

Slowly the man moved his hands toward the bushes, but his glance did not turn from the place made sinister by the warning rattle. His fingers unguided sought for a stick of weight and strength. Presently they closed about one that seemed adequate, and holding this weapon poised before him, the man moved slowly forward, glaring. The dog with his nervous nostrils fairly fluttering moved warily, one foot at a time, after his master.

But when the man came upon the snake, his body underwent a shock as from a revelation, as if after all he had been ambushed. With a blanched face, he sprang backward and his breath came in strained gasps, his chest heaving as if he were in the performance of an extraordinary muscular trial. His arm with the stick made a spasmodic defensive gesture.

The snake had apparently been crossing the path in some mystic travel when to his sense there came the knowledge of the coming of his foes. The dull vibration perhaps informed him and he flung his body to face the danger. He had no knowledge of paths; he had no wit to tell him to slink noiselessly into the bushes. He knew that his implacable enemies were approaching; no doubt they were seeking him, hunting him. And so he cried his cry, an incredibly swift jangle of tiny bells, as burdened with pathos as the hammering upon quaint cymbals by the Chinese at war—for, indeed, it was usually his death-music.

"Beware! Beware! Beware!"

The man and the snake confronted each other. In the man's eyes were hatred and fear. In the snake's eyes were hatred and fear. These enemies maneuvered, each preparing to kill. It was to be battle without mercy. Neither knew of mercy for such a situation. In the man was all the wild strength of the terror of his ancestors, of his race, of his kind. A deadly repulsion had been handed from man to man through long dim centuries. This was another detail of a war that had begun evidently when first there were men and snakes. Individuals who do not participate in this strife incur the investigations of scientists. Once there was a man and a snake who were friends, and at the end, the man lay dead with the marks of the snake's caress just over his East Indian heart. In the formation of devices hideous and horrible, nature reached her supreme point in the making of the snake, so that priests who really paint hell well, fill it with snakes instead of fire. These curving forms, these scintillant colorings create at once, upon sight, more relentless animosities than do shake barbaric tribes. To be born a snake is to be thrust into a place a-swarm with formidable foes. To gain an appreciation of it, view hell as pictured by priests who are really skilful.

As for this snake in the pathway, there was a double curve some inches back of its head which, merely by the potency of its lines, made the man feel with tenfold eloquence the touch of the death-fingers at the nape of his neck. The reptile's head was waving slowly from side to side and its hot eyes flashed like little murder-lights. Always in the air was the dry shrill whistling of the rattles.

"Beware! Beware! Beware!"

The man made a preliminary feint with his stick. Instantly the snake's heavy head and neck were bended back on the double curve, and instantly the snake's body shot forward in a low straight hard spring. The man jumped backward with a convulsive chatter and swung his stick. The blind, sweeping blow fell upon the snake's head and hurled him so that steel-colored plates were for a moment uppermost. But he rallied swiftly, agilely, and again the head and neck bended back to the double curve, and the steaming wide-open mouth made its desperate effort to reach its enemy. This attack, it could be seen, was despairing, but it was nevertheless impetuous, gallant, ferocious, of the same quality as the charge of the lone chief when the walls of white faces close upon him in the mountains. The stick swung unerringly again and the snake, mutilated, torn, whirled himself into the last coil.

And now the man went sheer raving mad from the emotions of his forefathers and from his own. He came to close quarters. He gripped the stick with his two hands and made it speed like a flail. The snake, tumbling in the anguish of final despair, fought, bit, flung itself upon this stick which was taking its life.

At the end, the man clutched his stick and stood watching in silence. The dog came slowly and with infinite caution stretched his nose forward, sniffing. The hair upon his neck and back moved and ruffled as if a sharp wind was blowing. The last muscular quivers of the snake were causing the rattles to still sound their treble cry, the shrill, ringing war-chant and hymn of the grave of the thing that faces foes at once countless, implacable and superior.

"Well, Rover," said the man, turning to the dog with a grin of victory, "we'll carry Mr. Snake home to show the girls."

His hands still trembled from the strain of the encounter, but he pried with his stick under the body of the snake and hoisted the limp thing upon it. He resumed his march along the path, and the dog walked, tranquilly meditative, at his master's heels.

The Fables

THE MESMERIC MOUNTAIN

A TALE OF SULLIVAN COUNTY

O N the brow of a pine-plumed hillock there sat a little man with his back against a tree. A venerable pipe hung from his mouth, and smoke-wreaths curled slowly skyward. He was muttering to himself with his eyes fixed on an irregular black opening in the green wall of forest at the foot of the hill. Two vague waggon ruts led into the shadows. The little man took his pipe in his hands and addressed the listening pines.

"I wonder what the devil it leads to," said he.

A grey, fat rabbit came lazily from a thicket and sat in the opening. Softly stroking his stomach with his paw, he looked at the little man in a thoughtful manner. The little man threw a stone, and the rabbit blinked and ran through an opening. Green, shadowy portals seemed to close behind him.

The little man started. "He's gone down that roadway," he said with ecstatic mystery to the pines. He sat a long time and contemplated the door to the forest. Finally, he arose and, awakening his limbs, started away. But he stopped and looked back.

"I can't imagine what it leads to," muttered he. He trudged over the brown mats of pine needles to where, in a fringe of laurel, a tent was pitched, and merry flames caroused

Text adheres to the English spelling of the text in *Last Words* (London, 1902).

about some logs. A pudgy man was fuming over a collection of tin dishes. He came forward and waved a plate furiously in the little man's face.

"I've washed the dishes for three days. What do you think I am—"

He ended a red oration with a roar: "Damned if I do it any more."

The little man gazed dim-eyed away. "I've been wonderin' what it leads to."

"What?"

"That road out yonder. I've been wonderin' what it leads to. Maybe some discovery or something," said the little man.

The pudgy man laughed. "You're an idiot. It leads to ol' Jim Boyd's over on the Lumberland Pike."

"Ho!" said the little man. "I don't believe that."

The pudgy man swore. "Fool, what does it lead to, then?"

"I don't know just what, but I'm sure it leads to something great or something. It looks like it."

While the pudgy man was cursing, two more men came from obscurity with fish dangling from birch twigs. The pudgy man made an obviously herculean struggle and a meal was prepared. As he was drinking his cup of coffee, he suddenly spilled it and swore. The little man was wandering off.

"He's gone to look at that hole," cried the pudgy man.

The little man went to the edge of the pine-plumed hillock and, sitting down, began to make smoke and regard the door to the forest. There was stillness for an hour.

Compact clouds hung unstirred in the sky. The pines stood motionless and pondering.

Suddenly the little man slapped his knee and bit his tongue. He stood up and determinedly filled his pipe, rolling his eye over the bowl to the doorway. Keeping his eyes fixed, he slid dangerously to the foot of the hillock and walked down the waggon ruts. A moment later he passed from the noise of the sunshine to the gloom of the woods.

The green portals closed, shutting out live things. The little man trudged on alone.

Tall tangled grass grew in the roadway, and the trees bended obstructing branches. The little man followed on over pine-clothed ridges and down through water-soaked swales. His shoes were cut by rocks of the mountains, and he sank ankle-deep in mud and moss of swamps. A curve just ahead lured him miles.

Finally, as he wended the side of a ridge, the road disappeared from beneath his feet. He battled with hordes of ignorant bushes on his way to knolls and solitary trees which invited him. Once he came to a tall, bearded pine. He climbed it, and perceived in the distance a peak. He uttered an ejaculation and fell out.

He scrambled to his feet and said: "That's Jones's Mountain, I guess. It's about six miles from our camp as the crow flies."

He changed his course away from the mountain, and attacked the bushes again. He climbed over great logs, golden-brown in decay, and was opposed by thickets of dark-green laurel. A brook slid through the ooze of a swamp, cedars and hemlocks hung their sprays to the edges of pools.

The little man began to stagger in his walk. After a time he stopped and mopped his brow.

"My legs are about to shrivel up and drop off," he said. ". . . Still, if I keep on in this direction, I am safe to strike the Lumberland Pike before sundown."

He dived at a clump of tag-alders and, emerging, confronted Jones's Mountain.

The wanderer sat down in a clear place and fixed his eyes on the summit. His mouth opened widely, and his body swayed at times. The little man and the peak stared in silence.

A lazy lake lay asleep near the foot of the mountain. In its bed of water-grass some frogs leered at the sky and crooned. The sun sank in red silence, and the shadows of the pines grew formidable. The expectant hush of evening, as if something were going to sing a hymn, fell upon the peak and the little man.

A leaping pickerel off on the water created a silver circle that was lost in black shadows. The little man shook himself and started to his feet, crying: "For the love of Mike, there's eyes in this mountain! I feel 'em! Eyes!"

He fell on his face.

When he looked again, he immediately sprang erect and ran.

"It's comin'!"

The mountain was approaching.

The little man scurried, sobbing through the thick growth. He felt his brain turning to water. He vanquished brambles with mighty bounds.

But after a time he came again to the foot of the mountain.

"God!" he howled, "it's been follerin' me," He grovelled.

Casting his eyes upward made circles swirl in his blood.

"I'm shackled I guess," he moaned. As he felt the heel of the mountain about to crush his head, he sprang again to his feet. He grasped a handful of small stones and hurled them.

"Damn you!" he shrieked loudly. The pebbles rang against the face of the mountain.

The little man then made an attack. He climbed with hands and feet wildly. Brambles forced him back and stones slid from beneath his feet. The peak swayed and tottered, and was ever about to smite with a granite arm. The summit was a blaze of red wrath.

But the little man at last reached the top. Immediately he swaggered with valour to the edge of the cliff. His hands were scornfully in his pockets.

He gazed at the western horizon, edged sharply against a yellow sky. "Ho!" he said. "There's Boyd's house and the Lumberland Pike."

The mountain under his feet was motionless.

HOW THE DONKEY LIFTED
THE HILLS

MANY PEOPLE suppose that the donkey is lazy. This is a great mistake. It is his pride.

Years ago, there was nobody quite so fine as the donkey. He was a great swell in those times. No one could express an opinion of anything without the donkey showing him where he was wrong in it. No one could mention the name of an important personage without the donkey declaring how well he knew him.

The donkey was above all things a proud and aristocratic beast.

One day a party of animals were discussing one thing and another until finally the conversation drifted around to mythology.

"I have always admired that giant, Atlas," observed the ox in the course of the conversation. "It was amazing how he could carry things."

"Oh, yes, Atlas," said the donkey. "I knew him very well. I once met a man and we got talking of Atlas. I expressed my admiration for the giant and my desire to meet him some day, if possible. Whereupon the man said that there was nothing quite so easy. He was sure that his dear friend, Atlas, would be happy to meet so charming a donkey. Was I at leisure next Monday? Well, then, could I dine with him upon that date? So, you see, it

Copyright, 1895, by Bacheller, Johnson & Bacheller.
Text is *Pocket Magazine:* June 1897. Reprinted in *Last Words* (London, 1902).

147

was all arranged. I found Atlas to be a very pleasant fellow."

"It has always been a wonder to me how he could have carried the earth on his back," said the horse.

"Oh, my dear sir, nothing is more simple," cried the donkey. "One has only to make up one's mind to it and then—do it. That is all. I am quite sure that if I wished I could carry a range of mountains upon my back."

All the others said, "Oh, my!"

"Yes I could," asserted the donkey, stoutly. "It is merely a question of making up one's mind. I will bet."

"I will wager also," said the horse. "I will wager my ears that you can't carry a range of mountains upon your back."

"Done," cried the donkey.

Forthwith the party of animals set out for the mountains. Suddenly, however, the donkey paused and said: "Oh, but look here! Who will place this range of mountains upon my back? Surely I cannot be expected to do the loading also."

Here was a great question. The party consulted. At length the ox said: "We will have to ask some men to shovel the mountains upon the donkey's back."

Most of the others clapped their hoofs or their paws and cried: "Ah, that is the thing."

The horse, however, shook his head doubtfully. "I don't know about these men. They are very sly. They will introduce some deviltry into the affair."

"Why how silly," said the donkey. "Apparently you do not understand men. They are the most gentle, guileless creatures."

"Well," retorted the horse, "I will doubtless be able to escape since I am not to be encumbered with any mountains. Proceed."

The donkey smiled in derision at these observations by the horse.

Presently they came upon some men who were laboring away like mad, digging ditches, felling trees, gathering fruits, carrying water, building huts.

"Look at these men, would you," said the horse. "Can you trust them after this exhibition of their depravity? See how each one selfishly—"

The donkey interrupted with a loud laugh.

"What nonsense!"

And then he cried out to the men: "Ho, my friends, will you please come and shovel a range of mountains upon my back?"

"What?"

"Will you please come and shovel a range of mountains upon my back?"

The men were silent for a time. Then they went apart and debated. They gesticulated a great deal.

Some apparently said one thing and some another. At last they paused and one of their number came forward.

"Why do you wish a range of mountains shovelled upon your back?"

"It is a wager," cried the donkey.

The men consulted again. And, as the discussion became older, their heads went closer and closer together, until they merely whispered, and did not gesticulate at all.

Ultimately they cried: "Yes, certainly we will shovel a range of mountains upon your back for you."

"Ah, thanks," said the donkey.

"Here is surely some deviltry," said the horse behind his hoof to the ox.

The entire party proceeded then to the mountains. The donkey drew a long breath and braced his legs.

"Are you ready?" asked the men.

"All ready," cried the donkey.

The men began to shovel.

The dirt and the stones flew over the donkey's back in showers. It was not long before his legs were hidden. Presently only his neck and head remained in view. Then at last this wise donkey vanished. There had been made no great effect upon the range of mountains. They still towered toward the sky.

The watching crowd saw the heap of dirt and stones make a little movement and then was heard a muffled cry.

"Enough! Enough! It was not two ranges of mountains. The wager was for one range of mountains. It is not fair! It is not fair!"

But the men only laughed as they shovelled on.

"Enough! Enough! Oh, woe is me— thirty snow-capped peaks upon my little back. Ah, these false, false men. Oh, virtuous, wise and holy men, desist."

The men again laughed. They were as busy as fiends with their shovels.

"Ah, brutal, cowardly, accursed men, ah, good, gentle and holy men, please remove some of those damnable peaks. I will adore your beautiful shovels forever. I will be a slave to the beckoning of your little fingers. I will no longer be my own donkey—I will be your donkey."

The men burst into a triumphant shout and ceased shovelling.

"Swear it, mountain-carrier!"

"I swear! I swear! I swear!"

The other animals scampered away then, for these men in their plots and plans were very terrible. "Poor old foolish fellow," cried the horse; "he may keep his ears. He will need them to hear and count the blows that are now to fall upon him."

The men unearthed the donkey. They beat him with their shovels. "Ho, come on, slave." Encrusted with earth, yellow-eyed from fright, the donkey limped towards his prison. His ears hung down like the leaves of the plantain during the great rain.

So now, when you see a donkey with a church, a palace, and three villages upon his back, and he goes with infinite slowness, moving but one leg at a time, do not think him lazy. It is his pride.